TIME

FOR

POETRY

REVISED EDITION

compiled

by

MAY HILL ARBUTHNOT

illustrated by Rainey Bennett

A Teacher's Anthology to accompany
THE NEW BASIC READERS
CURRICULUM

D1112740

Scott, Foresman and Company

ATLANTA   DALLAS   GLENVIEW   PALO ALTO   OAKLAND, N.J.

CONTENTS

WHY TAKE
TIME
FOR POETRY?

With all that the modern curriculum offers and demands, why should teachers take time for poetry? What does a child get from poetry that he does not get from prose? A child finds in poetry what an adult finds—an exhilaration that comes from the compatibility of ideas and form, from the melody and movement of the lines, from the little shivers of delight these qualities induce. More than any other type of literature, poetry has the power of arousing vivid sensory images and strong emotional responses. And more than any other kind of literary expression, poetry sensitizes a child's ear to the cadence of English words and the power and music of the English language.

Poetry is an aural art like music. It began generations ago as a speaking and listening experience. Someone spoke a poem; it caught the ear and was passed along by word of mouth for delight in its content, which, in turn, was made more exciting and more easily remembered by the swing and beat of the lines. So poetry lived. And so young children today respond enthusiastically when they hear verse read aloud and don't have to wrestle with its complexities on a printed page. Youngsters who are too soon put to reading it tend to become discouraged and to dislike it heartily, for poetry is undeniably more difficult to read than prose. Delayed meanings, parenthetical constructions, extreme condensation that requires much reading between the lines—all these make it so. If teachers want children to continue to enjoy poetry as they mature, then, in early years, poetry should be heard and not seen.

One of the primary purposes of this revised edition of *Time for Poetry*, as well as of the literature program in the *Guidebooks* that accompany The New Basic Readers, continues to be to help teachers help children become so familiar with poetry—both old and new—that they will grow naturally into young people and adults who like it and interpret it effectively for themselves. To reach this point, children must hear quantities of poetry read, must join in saying it themselves, and gradually learn to explore a new poem by reading it aloud until its movement, mood, and meaning come alive.

Happily, the first appeal of poetry to children and the key to reading it aloud effectively are found in what Walter de la Mare called "tune and runningness"—the melody and movement of poetry. To illustrate, read aloud a few times as simple a verse as "Ride a cock horse," and you will find yourself speaking in a sharply accented rhythm, and even moving your head from side to side as if you were really riding a galloping horse. Say the same verse to a two-year-old and see him begin to jounce his small body and wave his hands. Say it to a five- or six-year-old and watch him start off on a gallop of his own around the room or hear him join in saying the words with a fine galloping beat.

Such responses, such participation, are the joy of poetry and the means by which children learn to sense, as they grow older, the mood and meaning of more subtle verse. The smooth, flowing lines of Harry Behn's "This Happy Day," read as they were meant to be, bring a mood of happy serenity to the child who hears them. In distinct contrast, the lines of Frances Frost's "Night of Wind" call forth a different response because the lines are hurrying, breathless—accentuating feelings of danger, aloneness, and fear.

When a new book of poetry is explored, either for personal pleasure alone, or for the purpose of sharing that pleasure with children, the verses should be read aloud. Why? Because it is the poem's unique sound pattern that is the clue to its meaning. This is true from Mother Goose to Shakespeare. Unless the tempo, tone color, and cadence of a poem are captured (as they readily can be in meaningful oral reading), the poem never comes to life. But when these qualities are caught, they, in turn, prompt sensory images and emotional responses, reactions essential to complete understanding and appreciation of poetry. Sometimes the images are visual as in "the sun comes smiling up," or "the little fox . . . in the forest of fern." Sometimes they are auditory as in "the trample of wind." Sometimes they are kinesthetic as in "Ride a cock horse to Banbury Cross." And in many, if not most poems, sensory images fuse with emotional response to establish the action of the poem, to suggest its mood, or reinforce its idea. Certainly this is true of "This Happy Day" and "Night of Wind." Sensory imagery and emotional reaction are so closely related that it might be said that the more vivid the sensory imagery inspired by the lines of the poem, the deeper the emotional reaction to the poem will be. And it might be added that without sensory imagery and emotional reaction there can be no real understanding of poetry.

5

So basic is this point to the whole literature program that it will bear amplification. When a child hears poetry, or prose, and sees no illustrations, he enjoys it only to the extent that he can create his own mental pictures of the characters or action or situation. Miss Muffet comes alive for a child when he can see her, in his mind's eye, fleeing in terror from the big spider. Some children will show by their illustrations of the rhyme that they have visualized such details as the upset tuffet and the spoon and bowl flying through the air. The fun of Edward Anthony's *Oddity Land* verses comes from being able to see such ridiculous things as "an ox that always wears socks" and "mice that go skating on ice." The beauty of Jesse Stuart's "My Land Is Fair for Any Eyes to See" lies in visualizing "the purple hills" and "the fertile valley."

Although poetry depends upon visual imagery for much of its charm, auditory imagery is also important. The sounds of words in a poem can suggest action (the "jiggle, joggle, jee" in a poem about a train, for example); humor ("A flea and a fly in a flue" in a well-known limerick); mood ("All day I hear the noise of waters/ Making moan,/ Sad as the sea-bird is" in a poem about the sea). Furthermore, auditory imagery is an important aid to memory. When the *s*'s in "Sing a song of sixpence" whistle through a child's teeth, they sound and feel funny. The child doesn't know that this line makes a vivid auditory impression or that the *s*'s hissing behind his teeth as he says the words help him remember them later. But children will enjoy, even when they cannot analyze, the amusing auditory imagery roused by the onomatopoeia of such verses of early childhood as David McCord's pickety fence refrain and Rhoda Bacmeister's poem about a little girl who "splishes and sploshes/ And slooshes and sloshes" as she walks in slushy snow in her galoshes. Such poems prepare children to appreciate later on such curious auditory imagery as cottonwood leaves that "clap, clap, clap, in the dry night breeze."

Poets use imagery of taste, touch, and smell also—though to a lesser degree than visual and auditory imagery. Yet it is probably the imagined deliciousness of cocoa and ginger cookies more than anything else that establishes for children the feelings of warmth and peace and happiness in Gwendolyn Brooks' "Eunice in the Evening." Zhenya Gay's "The world is full of wonderful smells" arouses imagery of a series of familiar odors, from "applesauce and chocolate and a sugar bun," to a "dog when he's warm and lies in the sun." And a child can fully appreciate one of A. A. Milne's poems only when he re-creates the squishy, gritty feel of "Sand-Between-the-Toes."

One of the most important areas of sensory imagery in poetry is the kinesthetic. The melody and movement of poetry stimulate the initial response. When children hear many of the nursery rhymes read aloud, they soon discover that they can clap, walk, hop, skip, gallop, run, or rock to verse as successfully as they can to music. The young child who uses his arms or legs as he gallops to "Ride a cock horse" is being prepared to feel and understand later some of the adult poems of flight or haste that hurry the reader along on their insistent beat.

Carrying children from the level of tumpety-tump nursery rhymes to the place where they can and do read authentic poetry for themselves, giving them a wide variety of poetry—these are the purposes for which the poems in both the original and revised editions of *Time for Poetry* were compiled. The subject matter begins with the people, places, and interests of the child's everyday world. Here are Mother and Father, brothers and sisters, postmen and policemen. Here too are his favorite animals—kittens, dogs, rabbits, also elephants, tigers, kangaroos, and other creatures of forest, jungle, and zoo. The child's world of trains, planes, trucks, and boats, of skates and snow, early daffodils and valentines—the changing cycle of days and seasons are here, made more exciting and real by the magic of poetry. There are nonsense verses too, and the never-never world of make believe, and finally, to feed the growing spirit of the child, there are stray bits of beauty and wisdom. Each subject group begins with simple verses for the youngest child in school and progresses to richer, more mature poetry for children in the upper middle grades.

How are these poems to be used to bring children, step by step, toward the goal of poetry appreciation? First of all, every poem is to be read aloud to them. How to read these poems, how to develop poetry periods rich in enjoyment and increased understanding—these and many other details of method are discussed in the *Guidebooks* for The New Basic Readers. In addition, *Poetry Time,* an album of records for primary grades, gives teachers and children illustrations of different types of experiences with poetry. The record "Jigs and Jingles" invites children to respond to verses with appropriate bodily movements—jigs, gallops, skips. "Talking Time" asks them to join in speaking rhymes with the reader. "What Shall We Do Today?" and "In the Country" give children a variety of experiences in listening, through which they grow in understanding and appreciation of poetry that is a little more subtle. This album supplies ideas for the presentation of numerous verses in *Time for Poetry.*

7

Children who, from earliest years, continually hear poetry read effectively and who have a chance to join informally in saying it, will soon remember quantities of verse without any conscious effort. One child said, "You know, when I was walking home from school yesterday, I found myself saying 'The Pirate Don Durk of Dowdee' and I didn't even know that I knew it." Discovering the pleasure of saying poetry to oneself is one of the unexpected and valuable rewards of the poetry program outlined in the *Guidebooks* of The New Basic Readers and the *Poetry Time* records. Teachers will discover that poems can comfort or amuse children, can wake them up or quiet them, or can give them fresh courage when life seems a little grim.

Why, then, take time for poetry? Primarily, to develop a generation of children who thoroughly enjoy poetry and who can and do interpret it for themselves. But more than that. Poetry can become a shining armor against ugliness, vulgarity, and brutality. The miracle of the poems in this book is that they take many experiences of the child's world and give them a new importance, a kind of glory that they did not have when they were just experiences.

The child giggles at a dog "so furry I've not seen/ His face for years," is comforted by a pup that will "let you hold his little wiggly warmness" "when you've had a scold." He is sad for "Little things that run, and quail,/ And die in silence and despair." He goes "Skipping Along Alone" by the sea or he watches "Boats of mine a-boating," and wonders "Where will all come home?" He finds it pleasant "To say good morning to the sun" and quite natural to overhear a conversation between a goblin and a nymph. These poems carry him from skips and gallops to the world of dreams and aspirations. Time for poetry should be a time to lift young spirits and give them something to grow on. Poetry lovers do grow in grace and reverence for life because

> Loveliness that dies when I forget
> Comes alive when I remember.

And children remember poetry.

May Hill Arbuthnot

ALL SORTS OF PEOPLE

The ants are walking under the ground,
And the pigeons are flying over the steeple,
And in between are the people.

THE PEOPLE

The ants are walking under the ground,
And the pigeons are flying over the steeple,
And in between are the people.

Elizabeth Madox Roberts, *Under the Tree*
Copyright 1922 by B. W. Huebsch, Inc., 1950 by Ivor S. Roberts
Reprinted by permission of The Viking Press, Inc., New York

NEIGHBORLY

My Mother sends our neighbors things
   On fancy little plates.
One day she sent them custard pie
   And they sent back stuffed dates.

And once she sent them angel food
   And they returned ice cream;
Another time for purple plums
   They gave us devil's dream.

She always keeps enough for us
   No matter what she sends.
Our goodies seem much better
   When we share them with our friends.

And even if they didn't, why,
   It's surely lots of fun,
'Cause that way we get two desserts
   Instead of only one!

Violet Alleyn Storey
In *Child Life*, December 1926
By permission of the author and Rand McNally & Company

SONG

FOR MY

MOTHER

My mother has the prettiest tricks
　　Of words and words and words.
Her talk comes out as smooth and sleek
　　As breasts of singing birds.

She shapes her speech all silver fine
　　Because she loves it so.
And her own eyes begin to shine
　　To hear her stories grow.

And if she goes to make a call
　　Or out to take a walk,
We leave our work when she returns
　　And run to hear her talk.

We had not dreamed these things were so
　　Of sorrow and of mirth.
Her speech is as a thousand eyes
　　Through which we see the earth.

God wove a web of loveliness,
　　Of clouds and stars and birds,
But made not anything at all
　　So beautiful as words.

They shine around our simple earth
　　With golden shadowings,
And every common thing they touch
　　Is exquisite with wings.

There's nothing poor and nothing small
But is made fair with them.
They are the hands of living faith
That touch the garment's hem.

They are as fair as bloom or air,
They shine like any star,
And I am rich who learned from her
How beautiful they are.

Anna Hempstead Branch
The Shoes That Danced and Other Poems
Published by Houghton Mifflin Company, Boston, 1905

 Mother shake the cherry-tree,
Susan catch a cherry;
Oh how funny that will be,
Let's be merry!

One for brother, one for sister,
Two for mother more,
Six for father, hot and tired,
Knocking at the door.

Christina Georgina Rossetti, *Sing-Song*

ANDRE

I had a dream last night. I dreamed
I had to pick a Mother out.
I had to choose a Father too.
At first, I wondered what to do,
There were so many there, it seemed,
Short and tall and thin and stout.

But just before I sprang awake,
I knew what parents I would take.

And *this* surprised and made me glad:
They were the ones I always had!

Gwendolyn Brooks, *Bronzeville Boys and Girls*

"SH"

"Sh!" says mother,
"Sh!" says father.
"Running in the hall
Is a very great bother."

"Mrs. Grumpy Grundy,
Who lives down below,
Will come right up
First thing you know."

"Sh!" says father,
"Sh!" says mother.
"Can't you play a quiet game
Of some kind or other?"

James S. Tippett, *I Live in a City*

SHOP

WINDOWS

Mother likes the frocks and hats
And pretty stuffs and coloured mats.

Daddy never, never looks
At anything but pipes and books.

Auntie's fond of chains and rings
And all the sparkly diamond things.

Richard likes machines the best;
He doesn't care about the rest.

Nannie always loves to stop
In front of every single shop.

But I don't want to wait for a minute
Till we get to the one with the puppy dogs in it.

Rose Fyleman, *Gay Go Up*

SMELLS (*Junior*)

My Daddy smells like tobacco and books,
   Mother, like lavender and listerine;
Uncle John carries a whiff of cigars,
   Nannie smells starchy and soapy and clean.

Shandy, my dog, has a smell of his own
   (When he's been out in the rain he smells most);
But Katie, the cook, is more splendid than all—
   She smells exactly like hot buttered toast!

Christopher Morley, *The Rocking Horse*

The world is full of wonderful smells,
And you have a nose that always tells
Of bread in the oven, hot and nice,
Of cake being baked with lots of spice,
Of a barn with fresh-cut hay in the mows,
Of horses and pigs and cats and cows,
Of a dog when he's warm and lies in the sun,
Of applesauce and chocolate and a sugar bun.
Wouldn't it be dreadful if you'd no nose to tell
Of every wonderful, wonderful smell?

Zhenya Gay, *Jingle Jangle*
Copyright 1953 by Zhenya Gay
By permission of The Viking Press, Inc., New York

WALKING

When Daddy
Walks
With Jean and me,
We have a
Lot of fun
'Cause we can't
Walk as fast
As he,
Unless we
Skip and
Run!
I stretch,
And stretch
My legs so far,
I nearly slip
And fall—

15

But how
Does Daddy
Take such steps?
He doesn't stretch
At all!

Grace Ellen Glaubitz
In *Junior Home Magazine*
By permission of Child Training Association, Incorporated,
publishers of *Children's Activities*

AUTOMOBILE
MECHANICS

Sometimes
  I help my dad
Work on our automobile.
   We unscrew
   The radiator cap
    And we let some water run—
    Swish—from a hose
    Into the tank.

And then we open up the hood
And feed in oil
From a can with a long spout.
And then we take a lot of rags
And clean all about.
  We clean the top
  And the doors
  And the fenders and the wheels
  And the windows and floors. . . .
   We work *hard*
   My dad
   And I.

Dorothy Baruch, *I Like Machinery*
Harper & Brothers, New York, 1933

FATHER

My father's face is brown with sun,
His body is tall and limber.
His hands are gentle with beast or child
And strong as hardwood timber.

My father's eyes are the colors of sky,
Clear blue or gray as rain:
They change with the swinging change of days
While he watches the weather vane.

That galleon, golden upon our barn,
Veers with the world's four winds.
My father, his eyes on the vane, knows when
To fill our barley bins,

To stack our wood and pile our mows
With redtop and sweet tossed clover.
He captains our farm that rides the winds,
A keen-eyed brown earth-lover.

Frances Frost, *The Little Whistler*
Published by McGraw-Hill Book Company, New York, 1949
By permission of the author

What does the bee do?
   Bring home honey.
And what does Father do?
   Bring home money.
And what does Mother do?
   Lay out the money.
And what does baby do?
   Eat up the honey.

Christina Georgina Rossetti, *Sing-Song*

17

SLIPPERY

The six month child
Fresh from the tub
Wriggles in our hands.
This is our fish child.
Give her a nickname: Slippery.

Carl Sandburg, *Smoke and Steel*
Copyright 1920 by Harcourt, Brace and Company, Inc., New York
Renewed 1948 by Carl Sandburg

GROWNUPS

They're big,
They're broad,
They're tall,
They're strong.
Their hands are large,
Their legs are long.
And no one tells them
What to do.
I wish I were
A grownup, too.

For then I'd live
Without a care:
I'd never have to
Comb my hair;
I'd never have to
Nap at noon.
I'd like to be
A grownup soon.

William Wise, *Jonathan Blake*
Published by Alfred A. Knopf, Inc., New York
Copyright ©1956 by William Wise
By permission of author and publisher

SHOES

My father has a pair of shoes
So beautiful to see!
I want to wear my father's shoes,
They are too big for me.

My baby brother has a pair,
As cunning as can be!
My feet won't go into that pair,
They are too small for me.

There's only one thing I can do
Till I get small or grown.
If I want to have a fitting shoe,
I'll have to wear my own.

Tom Robinson, *In and Out*
Copyright 1943 by Tom Robinson
Reprinted by permission of The Viking Press, Inc., New York

FEET

I am a little boy.
When I go walking with my mother,
all I see is feet.

I get tired of seeing feet, feet, feet.
They make me dizzy.
When anybody speaks to me, I have to look
to see who it is.

Then my neck gets tired.
But some day I will grow up and see
faces.

Harry
From *Childcraft*, Vol. 8
© 1958 by Field Enterprises Educational Corporation
All Rights Reserved

ME   As long as I live
I shall always be
My Self—and no other,
Just me.

Like a tree—
Willow, elder,
Aspen, thorn,
Or cypress forlorn.

Like a flower,
For its hour—
Primrose, or pink,
Or a violet—
Sunned by the sun,
And with dewdrops wet.

Always just me.
Till the day come on
When I leave this body,
It's all then done,
And the spirit within it
Is gone.

Walter de la Mare, *Bells and Grass*
Copyright 1942 by Walter de la Mare
Reprinted by permission of The Viking Press, Inc., New York
By permission of the author and by Faber and Faber, Limited
(Also in *Rhymes and Verses* by Walter de la Mare
Published by Henry Holt and Company, Inc., New York, 1947)

In go-cart so tiny
  My sister I drew;
And I've promised to draw her
  The wide world through.

We have not yet started—
  I own it with sorrow—
Because our trip's always
  Put off till to-morrow.

Kate Greenaway, *Under the Window*
Frederick Warne and Company, New York and London, 1910

Little Blue Shoes
Mustn't go
Very far alone, you know.
Else she'll fall down,
Or, lose her way.
Fancy—what
Would Mamma say?
Better put her little hand
Under sister's wise command.
When she's a little older grown
Blue Shoes may go quite alone.

Kate Greenaway, *Marigold Garden*
Frederick Warne and Company, New York and London, 1910

21

LITTLE

I am the sister of him
And he is my brother.
He is too little for us
To talk to each other.

So every morning I show him
My doll and my book;
But every morning he still is
Too little to look.

Dorothy Aldis, *Everything and Anything*
Minton, Balch and Company, New York, 1927
Copyright 1925, 1926, 1927 by Dorothy Aldis

TWO IN BED

When my brother Tommy
Sleeps in bed with me,
He doubles up
And makes
himself
exactly
like
a
V

And 'cause the bed is not so wide,
A part of him is on my side.

Abram Bunn Ross
By permission of Mrs. A. B. Ross, Philadelphia

22

LITTLE BROTHER'S SECRET

When my birthday was coming
Little Brother had a secret:
He kept it for days and days
And just hummed a little tune when I asked him.
But one night it rained
And I woke up and heard him crying:
Then he told me.
"I planted two lumps of sugar in your garden
Because you love it so frightfully.
I thought there would be a whole sugar tree for
    your birthday.
And now it will all be melted."
O the darling!

Katherine Mansfield, *Poems*
Reprinted by permission of Alfred A. Knopf, Inc.
Copyright 1924 by Alfred A. Knopf, Inc.

GIRLS' NAMES

What lovely names for girls there are!
There's Stella like the Evening Star,
And Sylvia like a rustling tree,
And Lola like a melody,
And Flora like a flowery morn,
And Sheila like a field of corn,
And Melusina like the moan
Of water. And there's Joan, like Joan.

Eleanor Farjeon, *Over the Garden Wall*
Copyright 1933 by Eleanor Farjeon
Reprinted by permission of J. B. Lippincott Company
(Also in *Poems for Children* by Eleanor Farjeon
Published by J. B. Lippincott Company, Philadelphia and New York
Copyright 1951 by Eleanor Farjeon)

BOYS' NAMES

What splendid names for boys there are!
There's Carol like a rolling car,
And Martin like a flying bird,
And Adam like the Lord's First Word,
And Raymond like the Harvest Moon,
And Peter like a piper's tune,
And Alan like the flowing on
Of water. And there's John, like John.

Eleanor Farjeon, *Over the Garden Wall*

THE TWINS

The two-ones is the name for it,
And that is what it ought to be,
But when you say it very fast
It makes your lips say *twins*, you see.

When I was just a little thing,
About the year before the last,
I called it two-ones all the time,
But now I always say it fast.

Elizabeth Madox Roberts, *Under the Tree*

TIRED TIM

Poor tired Tim! It's sad for him.
He lags the long bright morning through,
Ever so tired of nothing to do;
He moons and mopes the livelong day,
Nothing to think about, nothing to say;
Up to bed with his candle to creep,
Too tired to yawn, too tired to sleep:
Poor tired Tim! It's sad for him.

Walter de la Mare, *Collected Poems, 1901–1918*

Copyright 1920 by Henry Holt and Company, Inc.
Copyright 1948 by Walter de la Mare
Reprinted by permission of the publishers
(Also in *Rhymes and Verses* by Walter de la Mare
Published by Henry Holt and Company, Inc., New York, 1947)

BUNCHES OF GRAPES

"Bunches of grapes," says Timothy;
"Pomegranates pink," says Elaine;
"A junket of cream and a cranberry tart
    For me," says Jane.

"Love-in-a-mist," says Timothy;
"Primroses pale," says Elaine;
"A nosegay of pinks and mignonette
    For me," says Jane.

"Chariots of gold," says Timothy;
"Silvery wings," says Elaine;
"A bumpity ride in a wagon of hay
    For me," says Jane.

Walter de la Mare, *Collected Poems, 1901–1918*

Copyright 1920 by Henry Holt and Company, Inc.
Copyright 1948 by Walter de la Mare
Reprinted by permission of the publishers
(Also in *Rhymes and Verses* by Walter de la Mare
Published by Henry Holt and Company, Inc., New York, 1947)

GRANDFATHER WATTS'S PRIVATE FOURTH

Grandfather Watts used to tell us boys
That a Fourth wa'n't a Fourth without any noise.
He would say, with a thump of his hickory stick,
That it made an American right down sick
To see his sons on the Nation's Day
Sit round in a sort of a listless way,
With no oration and no trained band,
No firework show and no root-beer stand;
While his grandsons, before they were out of bibs,
Were ashamed—Great Scott!—to fire off squibs.

And so, each Independence morn,
Grandfather Watts took his powder horn,
And the flintlock shotgun *his* father had
When he fought under Schuyler, a country lad.
And Grandfather Watts would start and tramp
Ten miles to the woods at Beaver Camp;
For Grandfather Watts used to say—and scowl—
That a decent chipmunk, or woodchuck, or owl
Was better company, friendly or shy,
Than folks who didn't keep Fourth of July.
And so he would pull his hat down on his brow,
And march for the woods, sou'east by sou'.

But once—ah! long, long years ago;
For Grandfather's gone where good men go—
One hot, hot Fourth, by ways of our own
(Such short cuts as boys have always known),
We hurried, and followed the dear old man
Beyond where the wilderness began—
To the deep black woods at the foot of the dump;
And there was a clearing and a stump—

26

A stump in the heart of a great wide wood;
And there on that stump our grandfather stood,
Talking and shouting out there in the sun,
And firing that funny old flintlock gun
Once in a minute, his head all bare,
Having his Fourth of July out there—
The Fourth of July that he used to know,
Back in eighteen-and-twenty, or so.

First, with his face to the heaven's blue,
He read the "Declaration" through;
And then, with gestures to left and right,
He made an oration erudite,
Full of words six syllables long;
And then our grandfather burst into song!
And, scaring the squirrels in the trees,
Gave "Hail, Columbia!" to the breeze.

And I tell you the old man never heard
When we joined in the chorus, word for word!
But he sang out strong to the bright blue sky;
And if voices joined in his Fourth of July,
He heard them as echoes from days gone by.

And when he had done, we all slipped back,
As still as we came, on our twisting track,
While words more clear than the flintlock shots
Rang in our ears. And Grandfather Watts?
He shouldered the gun his father bore,
And marched off home, nor'west by nor'.

H. C. Bunner, *Delsarte Recitation Book*

THE CUPBOARD

I know a little cupboard,
With a teeny tiny key,
And there's a jar of Lollipops
    For me, me, me.

It has a little shelf, my dear,
As dark as dark can be,
And there's a dish of Banbury Cakes
    For me, me, me.

I have a small fat grandmamma,
With a very slippery knee,
And she's Keeper of the Cupboard,
    With the key, key, key.

And when I'm very good, my dear,
As good as good can be,
There's Banbury Cakes, and Lollipops
    For me, me, me.

Walter de la Mare, *Collected Poems, 1901–1918*

Copyright 1920 by Henry Holt and Company, Inc.
Copyright 1948 by Walter de la Mare
Reprinted by permission of the publishers
(Also in *Rhymes and Verses* by Walter de la Mare
Published by Henry Holt and Company, Inc., New York, 1947)

OLD ELLEN SULLIVAN

Down in our cellar on a Monday and a Tuesday,
   You should hear the slapping and the rubbing and the muttering,
You should see the bubbles and the steaming and the splashing,
   The dark clothes dripping and the white clothes fluttering,
      Where old Ellen Sullivan,
      Cross Ellen Sullivan,
      Kind Ellen Sullivan,
Is washing and ironing, and ironing and washing.

Like a gnarled old root, like a bulb, brown and busy, 88668
   With earth and air and water angrily tussling,
Hissing at the flatirons, getting hot and huffy,
   Then up to the sunlight with the baskets bustling,
      Comes old Ellen Sullivan,
      Cross Ellen Sullivan,
      Kind Ellen Sullivan,
The clothes like blossoms, all sweet and fresh and fluffy.

Winifred Welles, *Skipping Along Alone*
The Macmillan Company, New York, 1931

WHERE'S MARY?

Is Mary in the dairy?
Is Mary on the stair?
What? Mary's in the garden?
What is she doing there?
Has she made the butter yet?
Has she made the beds?
Has she topped the gooseberries
And taken off their heads?
Has she the potatoes peeled?
Has she done the grate?
Are the new green peas all shelled?
It is getting late!
What? She hasn't done a thing?
Here's a nice to-do!
Mary has a dozen jobs
And hasn't finished two.
Well! here IS a nice to-do!
Well! upon my word!
She's sitting on the garden bench
Listening to a bird!

Ivy O. Eastwick, *Fairies and Suchlike*
Published and copyright 1946
by E. P. Dutton & Co., Inc., New York

29

PORTRAIT

BY

A NEIGHBOR

Before she has her floor swept
  Or her dishes done,
Any day you'll find her
  A-sunning in the sun!

It's long after midnight
  Her key's in the lock,
And you never see her chimney smoke
  Till past ten o'clock!

She digs in her garden
  With a shovel and a spoon,
She weeds her lazy lettuce
  By the light of the moon.

She walks up the walk
  Like a woman in a dream,
She forgets she borrowed butter
  And pays you back cream!

Her lawn looks like a meadow,
  And if she mows the place
She leaves the clover standing
  And the Queen Anne's lace!

Edna St. Vincent Millay, *A Few Figs from Thistles*

Published by Harper & Brothers
Copyright 1920, 1948 by Edna St. Vincent Millay

THE RAGGEDY MAN

O The Raggedy Man! He works fer Pa;
An' he's the goodest man ever you saw!
He comes to our house every day,
An' waters the horses, an' feeds 'em hay;
An' he opens the shed—an' we all ist laugh
When he drives out our little old wobble-ly calf;
An' nen—ef our hired girl says he can—
He milks the cow fer 'Lizabuth Ann.—
　　Ain't he a' awful good Raggedy Man?
　　　Raggedy! Raggedy! Raggedy Man!

W'y, The Raggedy Man—he's ist so good
He splits the kindlin' an' chops the wood;
An' nen he spades in our garden, too,
An' does most things 'at boys can't do.—
He clumbed clean up in our big tree
An' shooked a' apple down fer me—
An' nother'n', too, fer 'Lizabuth Ann—
An' nother'n', too, fer The Raggedy Man.—
　　Ain't he a' awful kind Raggedy Man?
　　　Raggedy! Raggedy! Raggedy Man!

An' The Raggedy Man, he knows most rhymes
An' tells 'em, ef I be good, sometimes:
Knows 'bout Giunts, an' Griffuns, an' Elves,
An' the Squidgicum-Squees 'at swallers therselves!
An', wite by the pump in our pasture-lot,
He showed me the hole 'at the Wunks is got,
'At lives 'way deep in the ground, an' can
Turn into me, er 'Lizabuth Ann!
　　Ain't he a funny old Raggedy Man?
　　　Raggedy! Raggedy! Raggedy Man!

The Raggedy Man—one time when he
Was makin' a little bow-'n'-orry fer me,
Says, "When *you're* big like your Pa is,
Air you go' to keep a fine store like his—
An' be a rich merchunt—an' wear fine clothes?—
Er what *air* you go' to be, goodness knows!"
An' nen he laughed at 'Lizabuth Ann,
An' I says " 'M go' to be a Raggedy Man!—
   I'm ist go' to be a nice Raggedy Man!"
     Raggedy! Raggedy! Raggedy Man!

James Whitcomb Riley

DOORBELLS

You never know with a doorbell
  Who may be ringing it—
It may be Great-Aunt Cynthia
  To spend the day and knit;
It may be a peddler with things to sell
  (I'll buy some when I'm older),
Or the grocer's boy with his apron on
  And a basket on his shoulder;
It may be the old umbrella-man
  Giving his queer, cracked call,
Or a lady dressed in rustly silk,
  With a card-case and parasol.
Doorbells are like a magic game,
  Or the grab-bag at a fair—
You never know when you hear one ring
  Who may be waiting there!

Rachel Field, *The Pointed People*
The Macmillan Company, New York, 1930

32

THE POSTMAN

Hey! the little postman,
  And his little dog,
Here he comes a-hopping
  Like a little frog;
Bringing me a letter,
  Bringing me a note,
In the little pocket
  Of his little coat.

Hey! the little postman,
  And his little bag,
Here he comes a-trotting
  Like a little nag;
Bringing me a paper,
  Bringing me a bill,
From the little grocer
  On the little hill.

Hey! the little postman,
  And his little hat,
Here he comes a-creeping
  Like a little cat.
What is that he's saying?
  "Naught for you to-day!"
Horrid little postman!
  I wish you'd go away!

Laura E. Richards, *Tirra Lirra*
Little, Brown & Company, Boston, 1932

Eight o'clock;
The postman's knock!
Five letters for Papa;
   One for Lou,
    And none for you,
And three for dear Mamma.

Christina Georgina Rossetti, Sing-Song

THE
SCISSOR-MAN

Sing a song of Scissor-men,
"Mend a broken plate,
Bring your knives and garden shears,
I'll do them while you wait.
Buzz-a-wuzz! Buzz-a-wuzz!
Fast the wheel or slow,
Ticker Tacker! Ticker Tack!
Rivets in a row."

Sing a song of Scissor-men,
Sitting in the sun,
Sing it when the day begins,
Sing it when it's done.
Be it hard or be it soft,
Here's a jolly plan;
Sing to make the work go well,
Like the Scissor-man.

Madeline Nightingale, Nursery Lays for Nursery Days
By permission of Basil Blackwell & Mott, Ltd., Oxford

THE NEW NEIGHBOR

Have you had your tonsils out?
    Do you go to school?
Do you know that there are frogs
    Down by Willow Pool?

Are you good at cricket?
    Have you got a bat?
Do you know the proper way
    To feed a white rat?

Are there any apples
    On your apple tree?
Do you think your mother
    Will ask me in to tea?

Rose Fyleman, *Gay Go Up*

Copyright 1929 by Doubleday & Company, Inc., New York
By permission of the publishers
and The Society of Authors, London,
as literary representatives of the Estate of the author

Oh, Susan Blue,
    How do you do?
Please may I go for a walk with you?
    Where shall we go?
    Oh, I know—
Down in the meadow where the cowslips grow!

Kate Greenaway, *Marigold Garden*
Frederick Warne and Company, New York and London, 1910

AT MRS. APPLEBY'S

When frost is shining on the trees,
    It's spring at Mrs. Appleby's.
You smell it in the air before
    You step inside the kitchen door.

Rows of scarlet flowers bloom
    From every window in the room.
And funny little speckled fish
    Are swimming in a china dish.

A tiny bird with yellow wings
    Just sits and sings and sings and SINGS!
Outside when frost is on the trees,
    It's spring at Mrs. Appleby's!

Elizabeth Upham McWebb
In *Child Life*, February 1945
Copyright 1945 by Child Life, Inc., Boston

Diana Fitzpatrick Mauleverer James
Was lucky to have the most beautiful names.
How awful for Fathers and Mothers to call
Their children Jemima!—or nothing at all!
But *hers* were much wiser and kinder and cleverer,
They called her Diana Fitzpatrick Mauleverer
                James.

A. A. Milne, *A Gallery of Children*
David McKay Company, Inc., New York, 1925
Renewal 1953 by A. A. Milne

MISS T.

It's a very odd thing—
    As odd as can be—
That whatever Miss T. eats
    Turns into Miss T.;
Porridge and apples,
    Mince, muffins and mutton,
Jam, junket, jumbles—
    Not a rap, not a button
It matters; the moment
    They're out of her plate,
Though shared by Miss Butcher
    And sour Mr. Bate;
Tiny and cheerful,
    And neat as can be,
Whatever Miss T. eats
    Turns into Miss T.

Walter de la Mare, *Collected Poems, 1901–1918*

P's the proud Policeman
    With buttons polished neat.
He's pleased to put his hand up
    When you want to cross the street.
By daylight he protects you;
    He protects you through the dark,
And he points the way politely
    To the playground or the park.

Phyllis McGinley, *All Around the Town*

MY POLICEMAN

He is always standing there
At the corner of the Square;
He is very big and fine
And his silver buttons shine.

All the carts and taxis do
Everything he tells them to,
And the little errand boys
When they pass him make no noise.

Though I seem so very small
I am not afraid at all;
He and I are friends, you see,
And he always smiles at me.

Once I wasn't very good
Rather near to where he stood,
But he never said a word
Though I'm sure he must have heard.

Nurse has a policeman too
(Hers has brown eyes, mine has blue),
Hers is sometimes on a horse,
But I like mine best of course.

Rose Fyleman, *The Fairy Green*

THE POLICEMAN

He never used to notice me
When I went by, and stared at him.
And then he smiled especially,
And now he says, "Hello there, Jim."

If he becomes a friend of mine,
And I learn all I ought to know,
Perhaps he'll let me turn the sign
And make the people Stop! and Go!

Marjorie Seymour Watts, *Do You Remember?*
Copyright 1927 by The Four Seas Co.
Reprinted by permission of Bruce Humphries, Inc.

THE BALLOON MAN

Our balloon man has balloons.
He holds them on a string.
He blows his horn and walks about
Through puddles, in the spring.

He stands on corners while they bob
And tug above his head—
Green balloons and blue balloons
And yellow ones, and red.

He takes our pennies and unties
The two we choose; and then
He turns around, and waves his hand,
And blows his horn again.

Dorothy Aldis, *Here, There and Everywhere*
Minton, Balch and Company, New York, 1927
Copyright 1927, 1928 by Dorothy Aldis

THE DENTIST

I'd like to be a dentist with a plate upon the door
And a little bubbling fountain in the middle of the floor;
With lots of tiny bottles all arranged in coloured rows
And a page-boy with a line of silver buttons down his clothes.

I'd love to polish up the things and put them every day
Inside the darling chests of drawers all tidily away;
And every Sunday afternoon when nobody was there
I should go riding up and down upon the velvet chair.

Rose Fyleman, *The Fairy Green*
Copyright 1923 by Doubleday & Company, Inc., New York
By permission of the publishers
and The Society of Authors, London,
as literary representatives of the Estate of the author

THE COBBLER

Crooked heels
  And scuffy toes
Are all the kinds
  Of shoes he knows.

He patches up
  The broken places,
Sews the seams
  And shines their faces.

Eleanor Alletta Chaffee
In *American Junior Red Cross News*, October 1938

40

MELONS

Melons! melons!
   All day long
Joe's mother sits
   Selling melons.
"Ho! ripe and rich!"
   Is her song,
All day long
   Selling melons.

Melons! melons!
   All day long
Joe walks the street
   Selling melons.
"Ho! ripe and sweet!"
   Is his song,
All day long
   Selling melons.

Mary Mapes Dodge

A PIPER

A piper in the streets to-day
Set up, and tuned, and started to play,
And away, away, away on the tide
Of his music we started; on every side
Doors and windows were opened wide,
And men left down their work and came,
And women with petticoats coloured like flame.
And little bare feet that were blue with cold,
Went dancing back to the age of gold,
And all the world went gay, went gay,
For half an hour in the street to-day.

Seumas O'Sullivan, *Collected Poems*
Orwell Press, Dublin, 1940

41

GYPSY JANE

She had corn flowers in her hair
    As she came up the lane;
"What may be your name, my dear?"
    "O, sir, Gypsy Jane."

"You are berry-brown, my dear."
    "That, sir, well may be,
For I live more than half the year,
    Under tent or tree."

Shine, Sun! Blow, Wind!
    Fall gently, Rain!
The year's declined, be soft and kind.
    Kind to Gypsy Jane.

William Brighty Rands

42

MEG MERRILIES

Old Meg she was a Gipsy,
    And liv'd upon the Moors:
Her bed it was the brown heath turf,
    And her house was out of doors.

Her apples were swart blackberries,
    Her currants pods o' broom;
Her wine was dew of the wild white rose,
    Her book a churchyard tomb.

Her Brothers were the craggy hills,
    Her Sisters larchen trees—
Alone with her great family
    She liv'd as she did please.

No breakfast had she many a morn,
    No dinner many a noon,
And 'stead of supper she would stare
    Full hard against the Moon.

But every morn of woodbine fresh
    She made her garlanding,
And every night the dark glen Yew
    She wove, and she would sing.

And with her fingers old and brown
    She plaited Mats o' Rushes,
And gave them to the Cottagers
    She met among the Bushes.

Old Meg was brave as Margaret Queen
    And tall as Amazon:
An old red blanket cloak she wore;
    A chip hat had she on.
God rest her aged bones somewhere—
    She died full long agone!

John Keats

43

DARK DANNY

Dark Danny has eyes
As black as the sloe,
And his freckles tell
Where the sunbeams go!

Dark Danny has hair
Like a raven's wing,
And his voice is gay
As the thrush in Spring.

Dark Danny will show
You the first wild rose;
Where the earliest violet
Blooms—he knows!

Where the red fox hides,
Why the nightingale sings . . .
Dark Danny knows all
These lovely things.

Ivy O. Eastwick, *Fairies and Suchlike*
Published and copyright 1946
by E. P. Dutton & Co., Inc., New York

THE SHEPHERD

How sweet is the shepherd's sweet lot!
From the morn to the evening he strays;
He shall follow his sheep all the day,
And his tongue shall be fillèd with praise.

For he hears the lambs' innocent call,
And he hears the ewes' tender reply;
He is watchful while they are in peace,
For they know when their shepherd is nigh.

William Blake, *Songs of Innocence*

44

THE GOATHERD

One day there reached me from the street
The sound of little trampling feet:
And through the dust and sunlight, I
Saw 'most a thousand goats go by.

The goatherd followed close behind:
He looked quite undisturbed and kind,
And Pablo said he knew him well,
And called him Señor Manuel.

His jacket was a shaggy skin,
And scarlet figures woven in
His blue zarape, made it gay
As though for a fiesta day.

His black eyes twinkled in the shade
That his broad-brimmed sombrero made:
And all his teeth were shiny bright
Like Mother's porcelain, and as white.

Before he went he took a drink
Of something very good, I think,
For he held up the gourd he wore
To Pablo's lips—then drank some more.

I told him there had seemed to be
At least a thousand goats, and he
Just laughed and said—to make a guess—
There *were* a thousand, more or less!

Grace Hazard Conkling, *Flying Fish*

45

THE COWBOY'S LIFE

The bawl of a steer,
To a cowboy's ear,
Is music of sweetest strain;
And the yelping notes
Of the gay coyotes
To him are a glad refrain.

For a kingly crown
In the noisy town
His saddle he wouldn't change;
No life so free
As the life we see
Way out on the Yaso range.

The rapid beat
Of his broncho's feet
On the sod as he speeds along,
Keeps living time
To the ringing rhyme
Of his rollicking cowboy song.

The winds may blow
And the thunder growl
Or the breezes may safely moan;—
A cowboy's life
Is a royal life,
His saddle his kingly throne.

Attributed to James Barton Adams
In *Cowboy Songs* (Compiled by J. A. Lomax)

NEW MEXICO

Out West is windy
And Out West is wide.
I pass villages of prairie dogs
On every horseback ride.

    I pass jack rabbits and sunsets
    And Pueblo Indians,
    And Mexicans in great big hats,
    And they are all my friends.

But when the moon comes sliding
And sagebrush turns to foam,
Then outdoors is Out West,
But indoors is Home.

Polly Chase Boyden

NOONDAY SUN

Oh, I've ridden plenty of horses
    And I've broken a score in my time,
But there never was one
    Like the colt Noonday Sun—
Now there was a horse that was prime!
    Oh, yippi ippi ai—Oh, yippi ippi ay,
Now there was a horse that was prime!

She'd run up the side of a mountain
    Or she'd tackle a wildcat alone.
Oh, she stood twelve hands high
    And her proud shining eye
Would soften the heart of a stone.
    Oh, yippi ippi ai—Oh, yippi ippi ay,
Would soften the heart of a stone.

She'd splash through a treach'rous river,
    Or she'd tease for an apple or sweet,
She'd buck and she'd prance,
    Or she'd do a square dance
On her four little white little feet.
    Oh, yippi ippi ai—Oh, yippi ippi ay,
On her four little white little feet.

But one night the rustlers stole her,
    They stole her and took her away.
Now the sun never shines,
    And the wind in the pines
Says, "You've lost your colt, lack-a-day!"
    Oh, yippi ippi ai—Oh, yippi ippi ay,
Says, "You've lost your colt, lack-a-day!"

Someday I'll ride through the prairie.
    Someday I'll pull out my gun,
And I'll plug him—bang-bang!—
    And I may even hang—
The outlaw who stole Noonday Sun.
    Oh, yippi ippi ai—Oh, yippi ippi ay,
The outlaw that stole Noonday Sun.

Oh, I still have her bridle and saddle,
    And I still have her bare empty stall.
But there'll never be one
    Like the colt Noonday Sun,
And she'll never more come to my call!
    Oh, yippi ippi ai—Oh, yippi ippi ay,
And she'll never more come to my call.

Kathryn and Byron Jackson, *Cowboys and Indians*

OPEN

RANGE

Prairie goes to the mountain,
   Mountain goes to the sky.
The sky sweeps across to the distant hills
And here, in the middle,
   Am I.

Hills crowd down to the river,
   River runs by the tree.
Tree throws its shadow on sunburnt grass
And here, in the shadow,
   Is me.

Shadows creep up the mountain,
   Mountain goes black on the sky,
The sky bursts out with a million stars
And here, by the campfire,
   Am I.

Kathryn and Byron Jackson, *Cowboys and Indians*

WHOOPEE TI YI YO

As I walked out one morning for pleasure,
I spied a cow-puncher all riding alone;
His hat was throwed back and his spurs was a-jingling,
And he approached me a-singin' this song,

Whoopee ti yi yo, git along little dogies,
It's your misfortune, and none of my own.
Whoopee ti yi yo, git along little dogies,
For you know Wyoming will be your new home.

Early in the spring we round up the dogies,
Mark and brand and bob off their tails;
Round up our horses, load up the chuck-wagon,
Then throw the dogies upon the trail.

It's whooping and yelling and driving the dogies;
Oh how I wish you would go on;
It's whooping and punching and go on little dogies,
For you know Wyoming will be your new home.

Some boys goes up the trail for pleasure,
But that's where you get it most awfully wrong:
For you haven't any idea the trouble they give us
While we go driving them along.

When the night comes on and we hold them on the bed-ground,
These little dogies that roll on so slow;
Roll up the herd and cut out the strays,
And roll the little dogies that never rolled before.

Oh, you'll be soup for Uncle Sam's Injuns;
"It's beef, heap beef," I hear them cry.
Git along, git along, git along little dogies,
You're going to be beef steers by and by.

Unknown
In *Cowboy Songs* (Compiled by J. A. Lomax)

POOR LONESOME COWBOY

I ain't got no father,
I ain't got no father,
I ain't got no father
To buy the clothes I wear.

I'm a poor, lonesome cowboy,
I'm a poor, lonesome cowboy,
I'm a poor, lonesome cowboy
And a long ways from home.

I ain't got no mother,
I ain't got no mother,
I ain't got no mother
To mend the clothes I wear.

I ain't got no sister,
I ain't got no sister,
I ain't got no sister
To go and play with me.

I ain't got no brother,
I ain't got no brother,
I ain't got no brother
To drive the steers with me.

I ain't got no sweetheart,
I ain't got no sweetheart,
I ain't got no sweetheart
To sit and talk with me.

I'm a poor, lonesome cowboy,
I'm a poor, lonesome cowboy,
I'm a poor, lonesome cowboy
And a long ways from home.

Unknown
In *Cowboy Songs* (Compiled by J. A. Lomax)

A SONG OF GREATNESS

When I hear the old men
Telling of heroes,
Telling of great deeds
Of ancient days,
When I hear that telling
Then I think within me
I too, am one of these.

When I hear the people
Praising great ones,
Then I know that I too
Shall be esteemed,
I too when my time comes
Shall do mightily.

Mary Austin, *The Children Sing in the Far West*

Reprinted by permission of and arrangement with
Houghton Mifflin Company, the authorized publishers

INDIAN CHILDREN

Where we walk to school each day
Indian children used to play—
All about our native land,
Where the shops and houses stand.

And the trees were very tall,
And there were no streets at all,
Not a church and not a steeple—
Only woods and Indian people.

Only wigwams on the ground,
And at night bears prowling round—
What a different place to-day
Where we live and work and play!

Annette Wynne, *For Days and Days*

Copyright 1919 by J. B. Lippincott Company

COTTONWOOD
LEAVES

Red firelight on the Sioux tepees,
    (Oh, the camp-smoke down the wind!)
Red firelight on the cottonwood trees
That clap, clap, clap in the dry night breeze.
    (Oh, the camp-smoke down the wind!)

Red-skinned braves in the circling dance;
    (Oh, the bright sparks toward the stars!)
The moccasined feet that stamp and prance
And the brandished knife and the lifted lance.
    (Oh, the bright sparks toward the stars!)

Eagle plumes in the swirling troop,
    (Oh, the wild flame leaping high!)
And the painted bodies ramp and stoop
To the drum's hot thump and the vaunting whoop.
    (Oh, the wild flame leaping high!)

Back where the darkness drops its veil
    (Oh, the sad smoke drifting low!)
The far wolves howl and the widows wail
For the graveless dead on the grim war trail.
    (Oh, the sad smoke drifting low!)

Night on the plains, and the dreams it weaves,
    (Oh, the embers black and cold!)
Where painted ghosts with the step of thieves
Dance to the clap of the cottonwood leaves.
    (Oh, the embers black and cold!)

Badger Clark, *Sky Lines and Wood Smoke*
The Chronicle Shop, Custer, S. D., 1947
Copyright 1935 by Francis Case
By permission of the author

53

HIAWATHA'S

CHILDHOOD

By the shores of Gitche Gumee,
By the shining Big-Sea-Water,
Stood the wigwam of Nokomis,
Daughter of the Moon, Nokomis.
Dark behind it rose the forest,
Rose the black and gloomy pine-trees,
Rose the firs with cones upon them;
Bright before it beat the water,
Beat the clear and sunny water,
Beat the shining Big-Sea-Water.
    There the wrinkled, old Nokomis
Nursed the little Hiawatha,
Rocked him in his linden cradle,
Bedded soft in moss and rushes,
Safely bound with reindeer sinews;
Stilled his fretful wail by saying,
"Hush! the Naked Bear will hear thee!"
Lulled him into slumber, singing,
"Ewa-yea! my little owlet!
Who is this, that lights the wigwam?
With his great eyes lights the wigwam?
Ewa-yea! my little owlet!"
    Many things Nokomis taught him
Of the stars that shine in heaven;
Showed him Ishkoodah, the comet,
Ishkoodah, with fiery tresses;
Showed the Death-Dance of the spirits,
Warriors with their plumes and war-clubs,
Flaring far away to northward

In the frosty nights of Winter;
Showed the broad, white road in heaven,
Pathway of the ghosts, the shadows,
Running straight across the heavens,
Crowded with the ghosts, the shadows.

At the door on summer evenings
Sat the little Hiawatha;
Heard the whispering of the pine-trees,
Heard the lapping of the water,
Sounds of music, words of wonder;
"Minne-wawa!" said the pine-trees,
"Mudway-aushka!" said the water.

Saw the fire-fly, Wah-wah-taysee,
Flitting through the dusk of evening,
With the twinkle of its candle
Lighting up the brakes and bushes,
And he sang the song of children,
Sang the song Nokomis taught him:
"Wah-wah-taysee, little fire-fly,
Little, flitting, white-fire insect,
Little, dancing, white-fire creature,
Light me with your little candle,
Ere upon my bed I lay me,
Ere in sleep I close my eyelids!"

Saw the moon rise from the water,
Rippling, rounding from the water,
Saw the flecks and shadows on it,
Whispered, "What is that, Nokomis?"
And the good Nokomis answered:

"Once a warrior, very angry,
Seized his grandmother, and threw her
Up into the sky at midnight;
Right against the moon he threw her;
'Tis her body that you see there."

Saw the rainbow in the heaven,
In the eastern sky, the rainbow,
Whispered, "What is that, Nokomis?"
And the good Nokomis answered:
  " 'Tis the heaven of flowers you see there;
All the wild flowers of the forest,
All the lilies of the prairie,
When on earth they fade and perish,
Blossom in that heaven above us."
  When he heard the owls at midnight,
Hooting, laughing in the forest,
"What is that?" he cried in terror;
"What is that?" he said, "Nokomis?"
And the good Nokomis answered:
"That is but the owl and owlet,
Talking in their native language,
Talking, scolding at each other."
  Then the little Hiawatha
Learned of every bird its language,
Learned their names and all their secrets,
How they built their nests in Summer,
Where they hid themselves in Winter,
Talked with them whene'er he met them,
Called them "Hiawatha's Chickens."
  Of all beasts he learned the language,
Learned their names and all their secrets,
How the beavers built their lodges,
Where the squirrels hid their acorns,
How the reindeer ran so swiftly,
Why the rabbit was so timid,
Talked with them whene'er he met them,
Called them "Hiawatha's Brothers."

Henry Wadsworth Longfellow, *The Song of Hiawatha*

THE PIONEER

Long years ago I blazed a trail
  Through lovely woods unknown till then
And marked with cairns of splintered shale
  A mountain way for other men;

For other men who came and came:
  They trod the path more plain to see,
They gave my trail another's name
  And no one speaks or knows of me.

The trail runs high, the trail runs low
  Where windflowers dance or columbine;
The scars are healed that long ago
  My ax cut deep on birch and pine.

Another's name my trail may bear,
  But still I keep, in waste and wood,
My joy because the trail is there,
  My peace because the trail is good.

Arthur Guiterman, *I Sing the Pioneer*
Copyright 1926 by E. P. Dutton & Co., Inc., New York
Renewal 1954 by Mrs. Vida Linda Guiterman
By permission of the publishers

BUFFALO DUSK

The buffaloes are gone.
And those who saw the buffaloes are gone.
Those who saw the buffaloes by thousands and
    how they pawed the prairie sod into dust
    with their hoofs, their great heads down
    pawing on in a great pageant of dusk,
Those who saw the buffaloes are gone.
And the buffaloes are gone.

Carl Sandburg, *Early Moon*
Copyright 1930 by Harcourt, Brace and Company, Inc., New York
Renewed 1948 by Carl Sandburg
By permission of the publishers

A
SONG
OF
SHERWOOD

Sherwood in the twilight, is Robin Hood awake?
Grey and ghostly shadows are gliding through the brake,
Shadows of the dappled deer, dreaming of the morn,
Dreaming of a shadowy man that winds a shadowy horn.

Robin Hood is here again: all his merry thieves
Hear a ghostly bugle-note shivering through the leaves,
Calling as he used to call, faint and far away,
In Sherwood, in Sherwood, about the break of day.

Merry, merry England has kissed the lips of June:
All the wings of fairyland were here beneath the moon,
Like a flight of rose-leaves fluttering in a mist
Of opal and ruby and pearl and amethyst.

Merry, merry England is waking as of old,
With eyes of blither hazel and hair of brighter gold:
For Robin Hood is here again beneath the bursting spray
In Sherwood, in Sherwood, about the break of day.

Love is in the greenwood building him a house
Of wild rose and hawthorn and honeysuckle boughs:
Love is in the greenwood, dawn is in the skies,
And Marian is waiting with a glory in her eyes.

Hark! The dazzled laverock climbs the golden steep!
Marian is waiting: is Robin Hood asleep?
Round the fairy grass-rings frolic elf and fay,
In Sherwood, in Sherwood, about the break of day.

Oberon, Oberon, rake away the gold,
Rake away the red leaves, roll away the mould,
Rake away the gold leaves, roll away the red,
And wake Will Scarlett from his leafy forest bed.

Friar Tuck and Little John are riding down together
With quarter-staff and drinking-can and grey goose-feather.
The dead are coming back again, the years are rolled away
In Sherwood, in Sherwood, about the break of day.

Softly over Sherwood the south wind blows.
All the heart of England hid in every rose
Hears across the greenwood the sunny whisper leap,
Sherwood in the red dawn, is Robin Hood asleep?

Hark, the voice of England wakes him as of old
And, shattering the silence with a cry of brighter gold,
Bugles in the greenwood echo from the steep,
Sherwood in the red dawn, is Robin Hood asleep?

Where the deer are gliding down the shadowy glen
All across the glades of fern he calls his merry men—
Doublets of the Lincoln green glancing through the May
In Sherwood, in Sherwood, about the break of day—

Calls them and they answer: from aisles of oak and ash
Rings the *Follow! Follow!* and the boughs begin to crash,
The ferns begin to flutter and the flowers begin to fly,
And through the crimson dawning the robber band goes by.

Robin! Robin! Robin! All his merry thieves
Answer as the bugle-note shivers through the leaves,
Calling as he used to call, faint and far away,
In Sherwood, in Sherwood, about the break of day.

Alfred Noyes, *Collected Poems*, Volume I

COLUMBUS

An Italian boy that liked to play
In Genoa about the ships all day,
With curly head and dark, dark eyes,
That gazed at earth in child surprise;
And dreamed of distant stranger skies.

He watched the ships that came crowding in
With cargo of riches; he loved the din
Of the glad rush out and the spreading sails
And the echo of far-off windy gales.

He studied the books of the olden day;
He studied but knew far more than they;
He talked to the learned men of the school—
So wise he was they thought him a fool,
A fool with the dark, dark, dreamful eyes,
A child he was—grown wonder-wise.

Youth and dreams are over past
And out, far out he is sailing fast
Toward the seas he dreamed;—strange lands arise—
The world is made rich by his great emprise—
And the wisest know he was more than wise.

Annette Wynne, *For Days and Days*
Copyright 1919 by J. B. Lippincott Company

WASHINGTON

He played by the river when he was young,
He raced with rabbits along the hills,
He fished for minnows, and climbed and swung,
And hooted back at the whippoorwills.
Strong and slender and tall he grew—
And then, one morning, the bugles blew.

Over the hills the summons came,
Over the river's shining rim.
He said that the bugles called his name,
He knew that his country needed him,
And he answered, "Coming!" and marched away
For many a night and many a day.

Perhaps when the marches were hot and long
He'd think of the river flowing by
Or, camping under the winter sky,
Would hear the whippoorwill's far-off song.
Working or playing, in peace or strife,
He loved America all his life!

Nancy Byrd Turner
In *Child Life,* February 1930
Copyright 1930 by Rand McNally & Company
By permission of the author

ANTHONY WAYNE

Down the Ohio the flatboats go,
  One by one and three in a row.
  "Wayne, Anthony Wayne!"
Faring still on the ancient quest,
Hundreds of flatboats drifting west.
  "Wayne, Anthony Wayne!"
The eddy swirls from the curving shores
And the steersmen chant as they shift their oars,
  "Wayne, Anthony Wayne!
Free is the river from source to mouth,
Free are the streams of the North and the South,
  Praise to Anthony Wayne!"

Wayne, Wayne, Anthony Wayne!
Who bore the brunt on Monmouth Plain,
Who marched by night with his picked command
And stormed Stony Point with spear in hand,
Who kept the steel of the bayonet bright,
Whose word in war was always, "Fight!"
  Wayne, Anthony Wayne!

Westward rode pirogue and raft,
  Freighted well with household gear,
Till the red man's hate and the red man's craft
  Stayed the march of the pioneer.

Shawnees lurked at the river shoals,
    Hurons claimed the woods for theirs.
Round the hamlet's reeking coals
    Yelled the braves of the Delawares.

Whelming all and sparing none,
    Dark Miamis mocked the slain.
"Give me a man!" cried Washington.
    "I am the man!" said Wayne.

Wayne, Wayne, Anthony Wayne,
Fiery heart and cool, clear brain,
Deep in the wilds of the Northwest region
Marched at the head of his hard-drilled legion,
Pressing where two had failed before,
Bringing the choice of peace or war.

Iroquois, Ottawa, Chippeway
Back of the fallen timbers lay;
Wyandot, Shawnee, Delaware
Poured their shot from the sheltered lair.
Over the root-laced parapet
The legion stormed with the bayonet,
Hunting the warriors out and out;
Hard on the flank of the savage rout,
Leaping the trunks in their reckless course,
Thundered the mad Kentucky Horse,
Lunging, plunging, bridles ringing,
Pistols flashing, sabers swinging,
Till the woods were clear as a new-washed fleece
And the vanquished sachems sued for peace.

Down the Ohio the flatboats go,
One by one and three in a row.
    "Wayne, Anthony Wayne!"

With light canoes and blunt bateaux
Down the Ohio a flatboat goes.
  "Wayne, Anthony Wayne!"

Up in the bow in a rough-made chair
Granddad sits with his silver hair;
Safe in the waist is the placid cow,
The coop of fowls, the scythe and plow,
And the towhead children, five and more;
While staunch in the stern at the steering oar,
Brave and tall, is the man who goes
To a land new-cleared of ruthless foes,
With his strong-souled wife in her homespun
    dress
Who will make a home in the wilderness,
For they come of the same undaunted strain
  As Wayne, Anthony Wayne!

Arthur Guiterman, *I Sing the Pioneer*

THOMAS

JEFFERSON

1743-1826

Thomas Jefferson,
What do you say
Under the gravestone
Hidden away?

"I was a giver,
I was a molder,
I was a builder
With a strong shoulder."

Six feet and over,
Large-boned and ruddy,
The eyes grey-hazel
But bright with study.

The big hands clever
With pen and fiddle
And ready, ever,
For any riddle.

From buying empires
To planting 'taters,
From Declarations
To trick dumb-waiters.

"I liked the people,
The sweat and crowd of them,
Trusted them always
And spoke aloud of them.

"I liked all learning
And wished to share it
Abroad like pollen
For all who merit.

"I liked fine houses
With Greek pilasters,
And built them surely,
My touch a master's.

"I liked queer gadgets
And secret shelves,
And helping nations
To rule themselves.

"Jealous of others?
Not always candid?
But huge of vision
And open-handed.

"A wild-goose-chaser?
Now and again,
Build Monticello,
You little men!

"Design my plow, sirs,
They use it still,
Or found my college
At Charlottesville.

"And still go questing
New things and thinkers,
And keep as busy
As twenty tinkers.

"While always guarding
The people's freedom—
You need more hands, sir?
I didn't need 'em.

"They call you rascal?
They called me worse,
You'd do grand things, sir,
But lack the purse?

"I got no riches.
I died a debtor.
I died free-hearted
And that was better.

"For life was freakish
But life was fervent,
And I was always
Life's willing servant.

"Life, life's too weighty?
Too long a haul, sir?
I lived past eighty.
I liked it all, sir."

Rosemary Carr and Stephen Vincent Benét
In *A Book of Americans*

Published by Rinehart & Company, Inc.

BENJAMIN
FRANKLIN

1706-1790

Ben Franklin munched a loaf of bread while walking down the street
And all the Philadelphia girls tee-heed to see him eat,
A country boy come up to town with eyes as big as saucers
At the ladies in their furbelows, the gempmun on their horses.

Ben Franklin wrote an almanac, a smile upon his lip,
It told you when to plant your corn and how to cure the pip,
But he salted it and seasoned it with proverbs sly and sage,
And people read "Poor Richard" till Poor Richard was the rage.

Ben Franklin made a pretty kite and flew it in the air
To call upon a thunderstorm that happened to be there,
—And all our humming dynamos and our electric light
Go back to what Ben Franklin found the day he flew his kite.

Ben Franklin was the sort of man that people like to see,
For he was very clever but as human as could be.
He had an eye for pretty girls, a palate for good wine,
And all the court of France were glad to ask him in to dine.

But it didn't make him stuffy and he wasn't spoiled by fame
But stayed Ben Franklin to the end, as Yankee as his name.
"He wrenched their might from tyrants and its lightning from the
    sky."
And oh, when he saw pretty girls, he had a taking eye!

Rosemary Carr and Stephen Vincent Benét
In *A Book of Americans*
Published by Rinehart & Company, Inc.
Copyright 1933 by Rosemary and Stephen Vincent Benét

A BALLAD OF
JOHNNY APPLESEED

Through the Appalachian valleys, with his kit a buckskin bag,
Johnny Appleseed went plodding past high peak and mountain crag.
Oh, his stockings were of leather, and his moccasins were tough;
He was set upon a journey where the going would be rough.

> See him coming in the springtime,
> Passing violets in the glade.
> Many apple trees are needed,
> And the pioneers want shade.

Johnny carried many orchards in the bag upon his back,
And the scent of apple blossoms always lingered in his track.
Over half a fertile continent he planted shiny seed;
He would toss them in the clearings where the fawn and yearling
    feed.

> In the summer see him tramping
> Through the windings of the wood.
> Big red apples in the oven
> Make the venison taste good.

He would wander over mountain; he would brave a raging stream,
For his eyes were filled with visions like an ancient prophet's dream.
He would travel after nightfall, start again at early morn;
He was planting seeds of apples for the children yet unborn.

> Where the autumn leaves turned crimson,
> He was eager to explore.
> Apple dumplings never blossomed
> On a shady sycamore.

Johnny traveled where the war whoop of the painted tribes rang loud;
And he walked among grim chieftains and their hot-eyed warrior
    crowd.

He told them of his vision, of his dream that would not die,
So he never was molested, and the settlers had their pie.

> Bitter winter found him trudging,
> Not for glory or applause,
> Only happy for the winesaps
> In tomorrow's applesauce!

Helmer O. Oleson

In *Story Parade*, November 1952
Copyright 1952 by Story Parade, Inc. Reprinted by permission

LINCOLN

There was a boy of other days,
A quiet, awkward, earnest lad,
Who trudged long weary miles to get
A book on which his heart was set—
And then no candle had!

He was too poor to buy a lamp
But very wise in woodmen's ways.
He gathered seasoned bough and stem,
And crisping leaf, and kindled them
Into a ruddy blaze.

Then as he lay full length and read,
The firelight flickered on his face,
And etched his shadow on the gloom.
And made a picture in the room,
In that most humble place.

The hard years came, the hard years went,
But, gentle, brave, and strong of will,
He met them all. And when to-day
We see his pictured face, we say,
"There's light upon it still."

Nancy Byrd Turner

In *Child Life*, February 1929
Copyright 1929 by Rand McNally & Company
By permission of the author

NANCY HANKS

1784-1818

If Nancy Hanks
Came back as a ghost,
Seeking news
Of what she loved most,
She'd ask first
"Where's my son?
What's happened to Abe?
What's he done?

"Poor little Abe,
Left all alone
Except for Tom,
Who's a rolling stone;
He was only nine
The year I died.
I remember still
How hard he cried.

"Scraping along
In a little shack,
With hardly a shirt
To cover his back,
And a prairie wind
To blow him down,
Or pinching times
If he went to town.

"You wouldn't know
About my son?
Did he grow tall?
Did he have fun?
Did he learn to read?
Did he get to town?
Do you know his name?
Did he get on?"

Rosemary Carr and Stephen Vincent Benét
In *A Book of Americans*

Published by Rinehart & Company, Inc.
Copyright 1933 by Rosemary and Stephen Vincent Benét

A REPLY TO NANCY HANKS

Yes, Nancy Hanks,
The news we will tell
Of your Abe
Whom you loved so well.
You asked first,
"Where's my son?"
He lives in the heart
Of everyone.

Julius Silberger
In *Children and Books*
Published by Scott, Foresman and Company, Chicago, 1947

I SAW A GHOST

As twilight fell
O'er the river's banks,
I saw the ghost
Of Nancy Hanks
Floating in mist
O'er the river's banks.

I told the ghost
Of Nancy Hanks
Floating in mist
O'er the river's banks,
How Abe saved our nation
And kept it one,
How slaves were made free
By a great man; her son.

As moonlight fell
O'er the river's banks,
The smiling ghost
Of Nancy Hanks
Faded in mist
O'er the river's banks.

Joan Boilleau
In *Children and Books*
Published by Scott, Foresman and Company, Chicago, 1947

ABRAHAM

LINCOLN

Remember he was poor and country-bred;
  His face was lined; he walked with awkward gait.
Smart people laughed at him sometimes and said,
  "How can so very plain a man be great?"

Remember he was humble, used to toil.
  Strong arms he had to build a shack, a fence,
Long legs to tramp the woods, to plow the soil,
  A head chuck full of backwoods common sense.

Remember all he ever had he earned.
  He walked in time through stately White House doors;
But all he knew of men and life he learned
  In little backwoods cabins, country stores.

Remember that his eyes could light with fun;
  That wisdom, courage, set his name apart;
But when the rest is duly said and done,
  Remember that men loved him for his heart.

Mildred Plew Meigs
In *Child Life*, February 1936. Copyright 1936 by Rand McNally & Company
By permission of Marion Plew Ruckel

**ABRAHAM
LINCOLN**

1809-1865

Lincoln was a long man.
He liked out of doors.
He liked the wind blowing
And the talk in country stores.

He liked telling stories,
He liked telling jokes.
"Abe's quite a character,"
Said quite a lot of folks.

Lots of folks in Springfield
Saw him every day,
Walking down the street
In his gaunt, long way.

Shawl around his shoulders,
Letters in his hat.
"That's Abe Lincoln."
They thought no more than that.

Knew that he was honest,
Guessed that he was odd,
Knew he had a cross wife
Though she was a Todd.

Knew he had three little boys
Who liked to shout and play,
Knew he had a lot of debts
It took him years to pay.

Knew his clothes and knew his house.
"That's his office, here.
Blame good lawyer, on the whole,
Though he's sort of queer."

"Sure, he went to Congress, once,
But he didn't stay.
Can't expect us all to be
Smart as Henry Clay.

"Need a man for troubled times?
Well, I guess we do.
Wonder who we'll ever find?
Yes—I wonder who."

That is how they met and talked,
Knowing and unknowing.
Lincoln was the green pine.
Lincoln kept on growing.

Rosemary Carr and Stephen Vincent Benét
In *A Book of Americans*

Published by Rinehart & Company, Inc.
Copyright 1933 by Rosemary and Stephen Vincent Benét

ALEXANDER GRAHAM BELL DID NOT INVENT THE TELEPHONE

Alexander Graham Bell
Did not invent the telephone,
No good thing was ever yet
The work of any man alone.

My old Grandmother Sarah Bates,
Halfway out from coast to sky,
On Bates's Island, had a fine
Hand in that electric pie.

Grandma Bates with a small child
On her lap with quick hot breath
Willed the telephone to be
As she sat and stood off death.

Another grandmother I had,
Her head all over gimlet curls,
Ran that road of whispers to
Three other merry little girls.

Your Grandmother Fisher with her man
Down with fever of the lung
Willed that wiry line of life
Through the woodlands to be hung.

Your other Grandma Mary Snow,
Miles from your tall father's sire,
Sent out her love so stout, so straight,
It turned into a singing wire.

Little lonely barefoot boys
Aching for their freckled kind,
Old farmers through long nights of snow
Unrolled that wire from their mind.

Alexander Graham Bell
Had lots of help at his strange labor,
Maybe an arm down through the clouds
Helped him make the whole world neighbor.

Robert P. Tristram Coffin, *Collected Poems*

THE
ANIMAL
FAIR

I went to the animal fair,
The birds and beasts were there.

Bow, wow, wow!
Whose dog art thou?
Little Tommy Tinker's dog.
Bow, wow, wow!

Mother Goose

Pussy has a whiskered face,
Kitty has such pretty ways;
Doggie scampers when I call,
And has a heart to love us all.

Christina Georgina Rossetti, *Sing-Song*

THE EXTRAORDINARY DOG

When Mother takes me calling
I say, "Oh, please and please
Let's visit with the folks who own
The funny Pekinese!"

I walk around him softly
Upon my tipsy-toes;
He sits so queer and solemn there,
So scornful in the nose.

I wonder very often:
Suppose I gave a sneeze,
A loud "Kerchoo!"—what would he do,
The pompous Pekinese?

Nancy Byrd Turner, *Magpie Lane*

THE ORDINARY DOG

When Brother takes me walking
I cry, "Oh, hip, hooray!
We're sure to see the jolly pup
That joins us every day!"

His ears are raggy-shaggy;
His coat's a dusty brown;
He meets me like a cannon ball
And nearly knocks me down.

He tells me all his secrets,
With joyful jumpings-up.
I wish the pompous Pekinese
Could know the Jolly Pup!

Nancy Byrd Turner, *Magpie Lane*

JIPPY AND JIMMY

Jippy and Jimmy were two little dogs.
They went to sail on some floating logs;
The logs rolled over, the dogs rolled in,
And they got very wet, for their clothes were thin.

Jippy and Jimmy crept out again.
They said, "The river is full of rain!"
They said, "The water is far from dry!
Ki-hi! ki-hi! ki-*hi*-yi! ki-hi!"

Jippy and Jimmy went shivering home.
They said, "On the river no more we'll roam;
And we won't go to sail until we learn how,
Bow-wow! bow-wow! bow-*wow*-wow! bow-wow!"

Laura E. Richards, *Tirra Lirra*

PUPPY AND I

I met a Man as I went walking;
We got talking,
Man and I.
"Where are you going to, Man?" I said
  (I said to the Man as he went by).
"Down to the village, to get some bread.
  Will you come with me?" "No, not I."

I met a Horse as I went walking;
We got talking,
Horse and I.
"Where are you going to, Horse, to-day?"
  (I said to the Horse as he went by).
"Down to the village to get some hay.
  Will you come with me?" "No, not I."

I met a Woman as I went walking;
We got talking,
Woman and I.
"Where are you going to, Woman, so early?"
  (I said to the Woman as she went by).
"Down to the village to get some barley.
  Will you come with me?" "No, not I."

I met some Rabbits as I went walking;
We got talking,
Rabbits and I.
"Where are you going in your brown fur coats?"
  (I said to the Rabbits as they went by).
"Down to the village to get some oats.
  Will you come with us?" "No, not I."

I met a Puppy as I went walking;
We got talking,
Puppy and I.
"Where are you going this nice fine day?"
  (I said to the Puppy as he went by).
"Up in the hills to roll and play."
    "*I'll* come with you, Puppy," said I.

A. A. Milne, *When We Were Very Young*

VERN

When walking in a tiny rain
Across the vacant lot,
A pup's a good companion—
If a pup you've got.

And when you've had a scold,
And no one loves you very,
And you cannot be merry,
A pup will let you look at him,
And even let you hold
His little wiggly warmness—

And let you snuggle down beside.
Nor mock the tears you have to hide.

Gwendolyn Brooks, *Bronzeville Boys and Girls*

BINGO HAS AN ENEMY

Bingo is kind and friendly,
 A gentleman right to the core,
But he can't bear rats
And he hates all cats
 And the fuzzy brown dog next door.

There's a nice little girl who lives there,
 But they glare at us more and more;
So we never can call,
And the cause of it all
 Is the fuzzy brown dog next door.

Bingo is limping a little
 And one of his ears is sore,
He's rather a fright,
But, oh, what a sight
 Is the fuzzy brown dog next door!

Rose Fyleman, *Gay Go Up*

Copyright 1929 by Doubleday & Company, Inc., New York
By permission of the publishers
and The Society of Authors, London,
as literary representatives of the Estate of the author

THE HAIRY DOG

My dog's so furry I've not seen
His face for years and years:
His eyes are buried out of sight,
I only guess his ears.

When people ask me for his breed,
I do not know or care:
He has the beauty of them all
Hidden beneath his hair.

Herbert Asquith, *Pillicock Hill*

Reprinted by permission of The Macmillan Company
By permission also of the author and William Heinemann, Ltd.

THE BUCCANEER

Danny was a rascal,
  Danny was a scamp;
He carried off a lady doll
  And left her in the damp.

He took her off on Monday;
  On Wednesday in he came
And dumped her gayly on the floor
  Without a bit of shame.

He was not sad or humble,
  He begged nobody's pardon;
He merely barked: "A lady doll
  I found out in the garden!"

Nancy Byrd Turner, *Magpie Lane*
Copyright 1927 by Harcourt, Brace and Company, Inc., New York
Copyright 1956 by Nancy Byrd Turner

MY DOG

His nose is short and scrubby;
  His ears hang rather low;
And he always brings the stick back,
  No matter how far you throw.

He gets spanked rather often
  For things he shouldn't do,
Like lying-on-beds, and barking,
  And eating up shoes when they're new.

He always wants to be going
  Where he isn't supposed to go.
He tracks up the house when it's snowing—
  Oh, puppy, I love you so.

Marchette Chute, *Rhymes About Ourselves*
The Macmillan Company, New York, 1932

LITTLE PUPPY

Little puppy with the black spots,
Come and herd the flock with me.
We will climb the red rocks
And from the top we'll see
The tall cliffs, the straight cliffs,
The fluted cliffs,
Where the eagles live.
We'll see the dark rocks,
The smooth rocks,
That hold the rain to give us
Water, when we eat our bread and meat,
When the sun is high.
Little spotted dog of mine,
Come and spend the day with me.
When the sun is going down
Behind the pointed hill,
We will follow home the flock.
They will lead the way
To the hogans where the fires burn
And the square cornbread is in the ashes,
Waiting our return.

In *Navajo Indian Poems*
Transcribed by Hilda Faunce Wetherill
Published by Vantage Press, New York
By permission of the publisher

A MALTESE DOG

He came from Malta; and Eumêlus says
He had no better dog in all his days.
We called him Bull; he went into the dark.
Along those roads we cannot hear him bark.

From the Greek translated by Edmund Blunden
In *The Oxford Book of Greek Verse in Translation*

84

TOM'S LITTLE DOG

Tom told his dog called Tim to beg,
And up at once he sat,
His two clear amber eyes fixed fast,
His haunches on his mat.

Tom poised a lump of sugar on
His nose; then, "Trust!" says he;
Stiff as a guardsman sat his Tim;
Never a hair stirred he.

"Paid for!" says Tom; and in a trice
Up jerked that moist black nose;
A snap of teeth, a crunch, a munch,
And down the sugar goes!

Walter de la Mare, *Bells and Grass*

THE BANDOG

Has anybody seen my Mopser?—
   A comely dog is he,
With hair of the colour of a Charles the Fifth.
   And teeth like ships at sea,
His tail it curls straight upwards,
   His ears stand two abreast,
And he answers to the simple name of Mopser,
   When civilly addressed.

Walter de la Mare, *Collected Poems, 1901–1918*

SUNNING

Old Dog lay in the summer sun
Much too lazy to rise and run.
He flapped an ear
At a buzzing fly.
He winked a half opened
Sleepy eye.
He scratched himself
On an itching spot,
As he dozed on the porch
Where the sun was hot.
He whimpered a bit
From force of habit
While he lazily dreamed
Of chasing a rabbit.
But Old Dog happily lay in the sun
Much too lazy to rise and run.

James S. Tippett, *A World to Know*
Copyright 1933 by Harper & Brothers

DOGS

AND

WEATHER

I'd like a different dog
  For every kind of weather—
A narrow greyhound for a fog,
  A wolfhound strange and white,
With a tail like a silver feather
  To run with in the night,
    When snow is still, and winter stars are bright.

In the fall I'd like to see
In answer to my whistle,
A golden spaniel look at me.
But best of all for rain
A terrier, hairy as a thistle,
To trot with fine disdain
Beside me down the soaked, sweet-smelling lane.

Winifred Welles, *Skipping Along Alone*
The Macmillan Company, New York, 1931

LONE

DOG

I'm a lean dog, a keen dog, a wild dog, and lone;
I'm a rough dog, a tough dog, hunting on my own;
I'm a bad dog, a mad dog, teasing silly sheep;
I love to sit and bay the moon, to keep fat souls from sleep.

I'll never be a lap dog, licking dirty feet,
A sleek dog, a meek dog, cringing for my meat,
Not for me the fireside, the well-filled plate,
But shut door, and sharp stone, and cuff, and kick, and hate.

Not for me the other dogs, running by my side,
Some have run a short while, but none of them would bide.
O mine is still the lone trail, the hard trail, the best,
Wide wind, and wild stars, and hunger of the quest!

Irene Rutherford McLeod, *Songs to Save a Soul*
Chatto & Windus, London, 1915

THE ANIMAL STORE

If I had a hundred dollars to spend,
  Or maybe a little more,
I'd hurry as fast as my legs would go
  Straight to the animal store.

I wouldn't say, "How much for this or that?"—
  "What kind of a dog is he?"
I'd buy as many as rolled an eye,
  Or wagged a tail at me!

I'd take the hound with the drooping ears
  That sits by himself alone;
Cockers and Cairns and wobbly pups
  For to be my very own.

I might buy a parrot all red and green,
  And the monkey I saw before,
If I had a hundred dollars to spend,
  Or maybe a little more.

Rachel Field, *Taxis and Toadstools*
Copyright 1926 by Doubleday & Company, Inc.

I LOVE LITTLE PUSSY

I love little Pussy,
  Her coat is so warm,
And if I don't hurt her,
  She'll do me no harm;
So I'll not pull her tail,
  Nor drive her away,
But Pussy and I
  Very gently will play.

Jane Taylor

88

"Pussy-cat, pussy-cat,
  Where have you been?"
"I've been to London
  To visit the Queen."
"Pussy-cat, pussy-cat,
  What did you there?"
"I frightened a little mouse
  Under the chair."

Mother Goose

A KITTEN

He's nothing much but fur
And two round eyes of blue,
He has a giant purr
And a midget mew.

He darts and pats the air,
He starts and cocks his ear,
When there is nothing there
For him to see and hear.

He runs around in rings,
But why we cannot tell;
With sideways leaps he springs
At things invisible—

Then half-way through a leap
His startled eyeballs close,
And he drops off to sleep
With one paw on his nose.

Eleanor Farjeon, *Over the Garden Wall*

Copyright 1933 by Eleanor Farjeon
Reprinted by permission of J. B. Lippincott Company
(Also in *Poems for Children* by Eleanor Farjeon
Published by J. B. Lippincott Company, Philadelphia and New York
Copyright 1951 by Eleanor Farjeon)

TIGER-CAT TIM

Timothy Tim was a very small cat
Who looked like a tiger the size of a rat.
There were little black stripes running all over him,
With just enough white on his feet for a trim
On Tiger-Cat Tim.

Timothy Tim had a little pink tongue
That was spoon, comb and washcloth all made into one.
He lapped up his milk, washed and combed all his fur,
And then he sat down in the sunshine to purr,
Full little Tim.

Timothy Tim had a queer little way
Of always pretending at things in his play.
He caught pretend mice in the grass and the sand,
And fought pretend cats when he played with your hand,
Fierce little Tim!

He drank all his milk, and he grew and he grew.
He ate all his meat and his vegetables, too.
He grew very big and he grew very fat,
And now he's a lazy old, sleepy old cat,
Timothy Tim!

Edith H. Newlin

In *Another Here and Now Story Book,* by Lucy Sprague Mitchell
Published and copyright 1937 by E. P. Dutton & Co., Inc., New York

CAT

My cat
Is quiet.
She moves without a sound.
Sometimes she stretches herself curving
On tiptoe.

Sometimes she crouches low
And creeping.

Sometimes she rubs herself against a chair,
And there
   With a *miew* and a *miew*
    And a purrrr   purrrr   purrrr
   She curls up
   And goes to sleep.

My cat
Lives through a black hole
Under the house.
So one day I
Crawled in after her.
And it was dark
And I sat
And didn't know
Where to go.
And then—

Two yellow-white
Round little lights
Came moving . . . moving . . . toward me.
And there
With a *miew* and a *miew*
   And a purrrr   purrrr   purrrr
My cat
Rubbed, soft, against me.

   And I knew
   The lights
   Were MY CAT'S EYES
   In the dark.

Dorothy Baruch, *I Like Animals*
Harper & Brothers, New York, 1933

IN HONOUR

OF

TAFFY TOPAZ

Taffy, the topaz-coloured cat,
Thinks now of this and now of that,
But chiefly of his meals.
Asparagus, and cream, and fish,
Are objects of his Freudian wish;
What you don't give, he steals.

His gallant heart is strongly stirred
By clink of plate or flight of bird,
He has a plumy tail;
At night he treads on stealthy pad
As merry as Sir Galahad
A-seeking of the Grail.

His amiable amber eyes
Are very friendly, very wise;
Like Buddha, grave and fat,
He sits, regardless of applause,
And thinking, as he kneads his paws,
What fun to be a cat!

Christopher Morley, *Songs for a Little House*

THE MYSTERIOUS CAT

I saw a proud, mysterious cat,
I saw a proud, mysterious cat
Too proud to catch a mouse or rat—
Mew, mew, mew.

But catnip she would eat, and purr,
But catnip she would eat, and purr.
And goldfish she did much prefer—
Mew, mew, mew.

I saw a cat—'twas but a dream,
I saw a cat—'twas but a dream
Who scorned the slave that brought her cream—
Mew, mew, mew.

Unless the slave were dressed in style,
Unless the slave were dressed in style
And knelt before her all the while—
Mew, mew, mew.

Did you ever hear of a thing like that?
Did you ever hear of a thing like that?
Did you ever hear of a thing like that?
Oh, what a proud mysterious cat.
Oh, what a proud mysterious cat.
Oh, what a proud mysterious cat.
Mew . . . Mew . . . Mew.

Vachel Lindsay, *The Congo and Other Poems*
Copyright 1914, 1942 by The Macmillan Company
and used with their permission

CAT

The black cat yawns,
Opens her jaws,
Stretches her legs,
And shows her claws.

Then she gets up
And stands on four
Long stiff legs
And yawns some more.

She shows her sharp teeth,
She stretches her lip,
Her slice of a tongue
Turns up at the tip.

Lifting herself
On her delicate toes,
She arches her back
As high as it goes.

She lets herself down
With particular care,
And pads away
With her tail in the air.

Mary Britton Miller, *Menagerie*
Copyright 1928 by The Macmillan Company
and used with their permission

 "Who are *you?*" asked the cat of the bear.
"I am a child of the wood,
I am strong with rain-shedding hair,
I hunt without fear for my food,
The others behold me and quail."
Said the cat, "You are lacking a tail."

"What can you *do?*" asked the cat.
"I can climb for the honey I crave.
In the fall when I'm merry and fat
I seek out a suitable cave
And sleep till I feel the spring light."
Said the cat, "Can you see in the night?"

Said the cat, "*I* sit by man's fire,
But I am much wilder than you.
I do the thing I desire
And do nothing I don't want to do.
I am small, but then, what is that?
My spirit is great," said the cat.

Elizabeth Coatsworth, *Away Goes Sally*

LITTLE LADY WREN

Little Lady Wren,
Hopping from bough to bough,
Bob your tail for me,
Bob it now!

You carry it so straight
Up in the air and when
You hop from bough to bough
You bob it now and then.

Why do you bob your tail,
Hopping from bough to bough,
And will not bob it when I say,
"Bob it now!"?

Tom Robinson, *In and Out*

Wrens and robins in the hedge,
   Wrens and robins here and there;
Building, perching, pecking, fluttering,
   Everywhere!

Christina Georgina Rossetti, Sing-Song

THE
SECRET

We have a secret, just we three,
The robin, and I, and the sweet cherry-tree;
The bird told the tree, and the tree told me,
And nobody knows it but just us three.

But of course the robin knows it best,
Because he built the—I shan't tell the rest;
And laid the four little—something in it—
I'm afraid I shall tell it every minute.

But if the tree and the robin don't peep,
I'll try my best the secret to keep;
Though I know when the little birds fly about
Then the whole secret will be out.

Unknown

WHAT
ROBIN
TOLD

How do robins build their nests?
   Robin Redbreast told me—
First a wisp of yellow hay
In a pretty round they lay;
Then some shreds of downy floss,
Feathers, too, and bits of moss,
Woven with a sweet, sweet song,
This way, that way, and across;
   That's what Robin told me.

96

Where do robins hide their nests?
　Robin Redbreast told me—
Up among the leaves so deep,
Where the sunbeams rarely creep,
Long before the winds are cold,
Long before the leaves are gold,
Bright-eyed stars will peep and see
Baby robins—one, two, three;
　That's what Robin told me.

George Cooper

"TALENTS DIFFER"

"What are you doing there, Robin a Bobbin,
　Under my window, out in the blue?"
"Building my nest, O Little One, Pretty One,
　Doing the thing that you cannot do!"

"What are you doing now, Robin a Bobbin,
　Under my window, out in the blue?"
"Brooding my eggs, O Little One, Pretty One,
　Doing the thing that you cannot do!"

"What are you doing there, Robin a Bobbin,
　Under my window, out in the blue?"
"Feeding my nestlings, Little One, Pretty One,
　Doing the thing that you cannot do.

"And what are *you* doing, pray, Little One, Pretty One,
　What are you doing, tell me now true?"
"Sewing my patchwork, Robin a Bobbin,
　Doing the thing that *you* cannot do!"

Laura E. Richards, *Tirra Lirra*

MRS. PECK-PIGEON

Mrs. Peck-Pigeon
Is picking for bread,
Bob-bob-bob
Goes her little round head.
Tame as a pussy-cat
In the street,
Step-step-step
Go her little red feet.
With her little red feet
And her little round head,
Mrs. Peck-Pigeon
Goes picking for bread.

Eleanor Farjeon, *Over the Garden Wall*
Copyright 1933 by Eleanor Farjeon
Reprinted by permission of J. B. Lippincott Company
(Also in *Poems for Children* by Eleanor Farjeon
Published by J. B. Lippincott Company, Philadelphia and New York
Copyright 1951 by Eleanor Farjeon)

CHICKADEE

The chickadee in the appletree
Talks all the time very gently.
He makes me sleepy.
I rock away to the sea-lights.
Far off I hear him talking
The way smooth bright pebbles
Drop into water . . .
Chick-a-*dee-dee-dee* . . .

Hilda Conkling, *Poems by a Little Girl*
Copyright 1920 by J. B. Lippincott Company

THE WOODPECKER

The woodpecker pecked out a little round hole
And made him a house in the telephone pole.

One day when I watched he poked out his head,
And he had on a hood and a collar of red.

When the streams of rain pour out of the sky,
And the sparkles of lightning go flashing by,

And the big, big wheels of thunder roll,
He can snuggle back in the telephone pole.

Elizabeth Madox Roberts, *Under the Tree*
Copyright 1922 by B. W. Huebsch, Inc., 1950 by Ivor S. Roberts
Reprinted by permission of The Viking Press, Inc., New York

THE BLACKBIRD

In the far corner
close by the swings,
every morning
a blackbird sings.

His bill's so yellow,
his coat's so black,
that he makes a fellow
whistle back.

Ann, my daughter,
thinks that he
sings for us two
especially.

Humbert Wolfe, *Kensington Gardens*
Reprinted by permission of Doubleday & Company, Inc.
By permission also of Miss Ann Wolfe

CROWS

I like to walk
And hear the black crows talk.

I like to lie
And watch crows sail the sky.

I like the crow
That wants the wind to blow:

I like the one
That thinks the wind is fun.

I like to see
Crows spilling from a tree,

And try to find
The top crow left behind.

I like to hear
Crows caw that spring is near.

I like the great
Wild clamor of crow hate

Three farms away
When owls are out by day.

I like the slow
Tired homeward-flying crow;

I like the sight
Of crows for my good night.

David McCord, *Far and Few*

A bird came down the walk:
He did not know I saw;
He bit an angle-worm in halves
And ate the fellow, raw.

And then he drank a dew
From a convenient grass,
And then hopped sidewise to the wall
To let a beetle pass.

Emily Dickinson, *The Poems of Emily Dickinson*
Little, Brown & Company, Boston, 1939

THE
SNOW-BIRD

When all the ground with snow is white,
    The merry snow-bird comes,
And hops about with great delight
    To find the scattered crumbs.

How glad he seems to get to eat
    A piece of cake or bread!
He wears no shoes upon his feet,
    Nor hat upon his head.

But happiest is he, I know,
    Because no cage with bars
Keeps him from walking on the snow
    And printing it with stars.

Frank Dempster Sherman

WILD GEESE

I heard the wild geese flying
    In the dead of the night,
With beat of wings and crying
I heard the wild geese flying,
And dreams in my heart sighing
    Followed their northward flight.
I heard the wild geese flying
    In the dead of the night.

Elinor Chipp, *The City and Other Poems*
Copyright 1923 by The Four Seas Co.
Reprinted by permission of Bruce Humphries, Inc.

THE SANDHILL CRANE

Whenever the days are cool and clear
The sandhill crane goes walking
Across the field by the flashing weir
Slowly, solemnly stalking.
The little frogs in the tules hear
And jump for their lives when he comes near,
The minnows scuttle away in fear,
When the sandhill crane goes walking.

The field folk know if he comes that way,
Slowly, solemnly stalking,
There is danger and death in the least delay
When the sandhill crane goes walking.
The chipmunks stop in the midst of their play,
The gophers hide in their holes away
And hush, oh, hush! the field mice say,
When the sandhill crane goes walking.

Mary Austin, *The Children Sing in the Far West*
Reprinted by permission of and arrangement with
Houghton Mifflin Company, the authorized publishers

THE PHEASANT

A pheasant cock sprang into view,
A living jewel, up he flew.

His wings laid hold on empty space,
Scorn bulged his eyeballs out with grace.

He was a hymn from tail to beak
With not a tender note or meek.

Then the gun let out its thunder,
The bird descended struck with wonder.

He ran a little, then, amazed,
Settled with his head upraised.

The fierceness flowed out of his eyes
And left them meek and large and wise.

Gentleness relaxed his head,
He lay in jewelled feathers, dead.

Robert P. Tristram Coffin, *Strange Holiness*
Copyright 1935 by The Macmillan Company
and used with their permission

The sea gull curves his wings,
The sea gull turns his eyes.
Get down into the water, fish!
(If you are wise.)

The sea gull slants his wings,
The sea gull turns his head.
Get down into the water, fish!
(Or you'll be dead.)

Elizabeth Coatsworth, *Plum Daffy Adventure*
Copyright 1947 by The Macmillan Company
and used with their permission

103

GULL

Life is seldom if ever dull
For the lazy long-winged white Sea Gull.
  It is as interesting as can be;
He lies on the wind, a slender reed,
And wheels and dips for hours to feed
On scruffy fish and pickleweed
  And to smell the smell of the sea.

He wheels and dips: beneath his wings
The pirate grins, the sailor sings,
  As they ply the China Sea.
While cold winds grip a schooner's sail
And water spouts from a great White Whale,
Perched on a mast, he rides the gale—
  What a wonderful life has he!

William Jay Smith, *Boy Blue's Book of Beasts*

Copyright © 1956, 1957 by William Jay Smith
By permission of the author
and publisher, Little, Brown & Company, Boston

FEATHER OR FUR

When you watch for
Feather or fur
Feather or fur
Do not stir
Do not stir.

Feather or fur
Come crawling
Creeping
Some come peeping
Some by night
And some by day.
Most come gently
All come softly
Do not scare
A friend away.

When you watch for
Feather or fur
Feather or fur
Do not stir
Do not stir.

John Becker, *New Feathers for the Old Goose*
Published by Pantheon Books, Inc., New York, 1956

MOUSE

Little Mouse in gray velvet,
Have you had a cheese-breakfast?
There are no crumbs on your coat,
Did you use a napkin?
I wonder what you had to eat,
And who dresses you in gray velvet?

Hilda Conkling, *Poems by a Little Girl*
Copyright 1920 by J. B. Lippincott Company

105

MICE

I think mice
Are rather nice.

Their tails are long,
Their faces small,
They haven't any
Chins at all.
Their ears are pink,
Their teeth are white,
They run about
The house at night.
They nibble things
They shouldn't touch
And no one seems
To like them much.

But *I* think mice
Are nice.

Rose Fyleman, *Fifty-One New Nursery Rhymes*
Copyright 1931 by Doubleday & Company, Inc., New York
By permission of the publishers
and The Society of Authors, London,
as literary representatives of the Estate of the author

I was lying still in a field one day
When a tiny mouse came out to play.
His eyes were bright,
His tummy white,
His ears were neat,
And pink his feet,
His fur was brown,
And soft as down,
And his tail was long as he skipped away,
And I lay still to watch him play.

Zhenya Gay, *Jingle Jangle*
Copyright 1953 by Zhenya Gay
By permission of The Viking Press, Inc., New York

THE HOUSE OF THE MOUSE

The house of the mouse
is a wee little house,
a green little house in the grass,
which big clumsy folk
may hunt and may poke
and still never see as they pass
this sweet little, neat little,
wee little, green little,
cuddle-down hide-away
house in the grass.

Lucy Sprague Mitchell
In *Another Here and Now Story Book*
Published and copyright 1937
by E. P. Dutton & Co., Inc., New York

The city mouse lives in a house;—
  The garden mouse lives in a bower,
He's friendly with the frogs and toads,
  And sees the pretty plants in flower.

The city mouse eats bread and cheese;—
  The garden mouse eats what he can;
We will not grudge him seeds and stalks,
  Poor little timid furry man.

Christina Georgina Rossetti, *Sing-Song*

THE MOUSE

I heard a mouse
Bitterly complaining
In a crack of moonlight
Aslant on the floor—

"Little I ask
And that little is not granted.
There are few crumbs
In this world any more.

"The bread-box is tin
And I cannot get in.

"The jam's in a jar
My teeth cannot mar.

"The cheese sits by itself
On the pantry shelf—

"All night I run
Searching and seeking,
All night I run
About on the floor,

"Moonlight is there
And a bare place for dancing,
But no little feast
Is spread any more."

Elizabeth Coatsworth, *Compass Rose*

 I saw a little squirrel,
Sitting in a tree;
He was eating a nut
And wouldn't look at me.

Child in Winnetka Nursery
In *Very Young Verses*
Published by Houghton Mifflin Company
The editors of this book searched diligently to find the source
and to obtain permission to use this poem, but without success

JOE

We feed the birds in winter,
And outside in the snow
We have a tray of many seeds
For many birds of many breeds
And one gray squirrel named Joe.
　　But Joe comes early,
　　Joe comes late,
　　And all the birds
　　Must stand and wait.
And waiting there for Joe to go
Is pretty cold work in the snow.

David McCord, *Far and Few*
Copyright 1929, 1931, 1952 by David McCord
By permission of Little, Brown & Company, Boston

FRED

Speaking of Joe, I should have said
Our flying squirrel's name is Fred.

Fred is no flyer, but a glider.
His skin is loose and soft as eider.

But Fred himself is no softy:
He likes tough trees, and likes them lofty.

Fred is not around much at noon;
But at night, and under a bright full moon,

He sails from tree to tree like a circus performer;
And once last summer he sailed right into the dormer

Window of the empty house next door.
But that's Fred all over. Need I say more?

David McCord, *Far and Few*
Copyright 1929, 1931, 1952 by David McCord
By permission of Little, Brown & Company, Boston

109

THE SQUIRREL

Whisky, frisky,
Hippity hop,
Up he goes
To the tree top!

Whirly, twirly,
Round and round,
Down he scampers
To the ground.

Furly, curly
What a tail!
Tall as a feather
Broad as a sail!

Where's his supper?
In the shell,
Snappity, crackity,
Out it fell!

Unknown

THE STORY OF THE BABY SQUIRREL

He ran right out of the woods to me,
Little and furry and panting with fright;
I offered a finger just to see—
And both of his paws held on to it tight.

Was it dogs that had scared him? A crashing limb?
I waited a while but there wasn't a sign
Of his mother coming to rescue him.
So then I decided he was mine.

I lifted him up and he wasn't afraid
To ride along in the crook of my arm.
"A very fine place," he thought, "just made
For keeping me comfortable, safe and warm."

At home he seemed happy to guzzle his milk
Out of an eye dropper six times a day.
We gave him a pillow of damask silk
On which he very royally lay.

He frisked on the carpets, he whisked up the stairs
(Where he played with some soap till it made him sneeze).
He loved it exploring the tables and chairs,
And he climbed up the curtains exactly like trees.

He watched his fuzzy gray stomach swell.
He grew until he could leave a dent
In the pillow on which he'd slept so well—
And then . . . Oh, then one morning he went.

Perhaps a squirrel around the place
Adopted him: oh, we're certain it's true
For once a little looking down face
Seemed to be saying: "How do you do?"

Dorothy Aldis, *Before Things Happen*
G. P. Putnam's Sons, New York, 1939
Copyright 1939 by Dorothy Aldis

111

LITTLE
CHARLIE
CHIPMUNK

Little Charlie Chipmunk was a *talker*. Mercy me!
He chattered after breakfast and he chattered after tea!
He chattered to his father and he chattered to his mother!
He chattered to his sister and he chattered to his brother!
He chattered till his family was almost driven *wild!*
Oh, little Charlie Chipmunk was a *very* tiresome child!

Helen Cowles LeCron, *Animal Etiquette Book*
Frederick A. Stokes Company, 1926
By permission of the author

WHAT IS IT?

Tall ears,
Twinkly nose,
Tiny tail,
And—hop, he goes!

What *is* he—
Can you guess?
I feed him carrots
And watercress.

His ears are long,
His tail is small—
And he doesn't make any
Noise at all!

Tall ears,
Twinkly nose,
Tiny tail,
And—hop, he goes!

Marie Louise Allen, *A Pocketful of Rhymes*
Harper & Brothers, New York, 1939

RABBITS

My two white rabbits
Chase each other
With humping, bumping backs.
  They go hopping, hopping,
  And their long ears
    Go flopping, flopping.
      And they
      Make faces
      With their noses
      Up and down.

Today
I went inside their fence
To play rabbit with them.
And in one corner
Under a loose bush
I saw something shivering the leaves.
And I pushed
And looked.
And I found—
There
In a hole
In the ground—
Three baby rabbits
Hidden away.
      And *they*
      Made faces
      With their noses
      Up and down.

Dorothy Baruch, *I Like Animals*
Harper & Brothers, New York, 1933

MARKET SQUARE

I had a penny,
A bright new penny,
I took my penny
 To the market square.
I wanted a rabbit,
A little brown rabbit,
And I looked for a rabbit
 'Most everywhere.

For I went to the stall where they sold sweet lavender
(*"Only a penny for a bunch of lavender!"*).
"Have you got a rabbit, 'cos I don't want lavender?"
 But they hadn't got a rabbit, not anywhere there.

I had a penny,
And I had another penny,
I took my pennies
 To the market square.
I did want a rabbit,
A little baby rabbit,
And I looked for rabbits
 'Most everywhere.

And I went to the stall where they sold fresh mackerel
(*"Now then! Tuppence for a fresh-caught mackerel!"*).
"Have you got a rabbit, 'cos I don't like mackerel?"
 But they hadn't got a rabbit, not anywhere there.

I found a sixpence,
A little white sixpence.
I took it in my hand
    To the market square.
I was buying my rabbit
(I do like rabbits),
And I looked for my rabbit
    'Most everywhere.

So I went to the stall where they sold fine saucepans
(*"Walk up, walk up, sixpence for a saucepan!"*).
"Could I have a rabbit, 'cos we've got two saucepans?"
    But they hadn't got a rabbit, not anywhere there.

I had nuffin',
No, I hadn't got nuffin',
So I didn't go down
    To the market square;
But I walked on the common,
The old-gold common . . .
And I saw little rabbits
    'Most everywhere!

So I'm sorry for the people who sell fine saucepans,
I'm sorry for the people who sell fresh mackerel,
I'm sorry for the people who sell sweet lavender,
    'Cos they haven't got a rabbit, not anywhere there!

A. A. Milne, *When We Were Very Young*

And timid, funny, brisk little bunny,
Winks his nose and sits all sunny.

Christina Georgina Rossetti, Sing-Song

THE

RABBIT

When they said the time to hide was mine,
I hid back under a thick grapevine.

And while I was still for the time to pass,
A little gray thing came out of the grass.

He hopped his way through the melon bed
And sat down close by a cabbage head.

He sat down close where I could see,
And his big still eyes looked hard at me,

His big eyes bursting out of the rim,
And I looked back very hard at him.

Elizabeth Madox Roberts, Under the Tree

Copyright 1922 by B. W. Huebsch, Inc., 1950 by Ivor S. Roberts
Reprinted by permission of The Viking Press, Inc., New York

WHITE

SEASON

In the winter the rabbits match their pelts to the earth.
With ears laid back, they go
Blown through the silver hollow, the silver thicket,
Like puffs of snow.

Frances Frost, Pool in the Meadow

Reprinted by permission of and arrangement with
Houghton Mifflin Company, the authorized publishers

A STORY IN THE SNOW

This morning, as I walked to school
  Across the fluffy snow,
I came upon a bunny's tracks—
  A jumping, zigzag row.

He must have hurried very fast,
  For here and there I saw
Along his jerky, winding trail
  The print of Rover's paw!

I set my lunch pail on the snow
  And stood there very still,
For only Rover's clumsy tracks
  Led down the little hill.

Then suddenly I thought I heard
  A rustling sound close by;
And there within a grassy clump
  Shone Bunny's twinkling eye!

Pearl Riggs Crouch
In *Wee Wisdom*, January 1931
By permission of the author

THE HARE

In the black furrow of a field
I saw an old witch-hare this night;
And she cocked a lissome ear,
And she eyed the moon so bright,
And she nibbled of the green;
And I whispered "Whsst! witch-hare,"
Away like a ghostie o'er the field
She fled, and left the moonlight there.

Walter de la Mare, *Collected Poems, 1901–1918*
Copyright 1920 by Henry Holt and Company, Inc.
Copyright 1948 by Walter de la Mare
Reprinted by permission of the publishers
(Also in *Rhymes and Verses* by Walter de la Mare
Published by Henry Holt and Company, Inc., New York, 1947)

THE RABBITS' SONG OUTSIDE THE TAVERN

We, who play under the pines,
We, who dance in the snow
That shines blue in the light of the moon,
Sometimes halt as we go—
Stand with our ears erect,
Our noses testing the air,
To gaze at the golden world
Behind the windows there.

Suns they have in a cave,
Stars, each on a tall white stem,
And the thought of a fox or an owl
Seems never to trouble them.
They laugh and eat and are warm,
Their food is ready at hand,
While hungry out in the cold
We little rabbits stand.

But they never dance as we dance!
They haven't the speed nor the grace.
We scorn both the dog and the cat
Who lie by their fireplace.
We scorn them licking their paws,
Their eyes on an upraised spoon—
We who dance hungry and wild
Under a winter's moon.

Elizabeth Coatsworth, *Away Goes Sally*

118

THE SNARE

I hear a sudden cry of pain!
There is a rabbit in a snare:
Now I hear the cry again,
But I cannot tell from where.

But I cannot tell from where
He is calling out for aid!
Crying on the frightened air,
Making everything afraid!

Making everything afraid!
Wrinkling up his little face!
As he cries again for aid;
—And I cannot find the place!

And I cannot find the place
Where his paw is in the snare!
Little One! Oh, Little One!
I am searching everywhere!

James Stephens, *Songs from the Clay*

THE SKUNK

When the sun has slipped away
And the dew is on the day,
Then the creature comes to call
Men malign the most of all.

The little skunk is very neat,
With his sensitive, plush feet
And a dainty, slim head set
With diamonds on bands of jet.

He walks upon his evening's duty
Of declaring how that beauty
With her patterns is not done
At the setting of the sun.

He undulates across the lawn,
He asks nobody to fawn
On his graces. All that he
Asks is that men let him be.

He knows that he is very fine
In every clean and rippling line,
He is a conscious black and white
Little symphony of night.

Robert P. Tristram Coffin, *Saltwater Farm*

PRAIRIE-DOG TOWN

Old Peter Prairie-Dog
Builds him a house
In Prairie-Dog Town,
With a door that goes down
And down and down,
And a hall that goes under
And under and under,

Where you can't see the lightning,
You can't hear the thunder,
For they don't *like* thunder
In Prairie-Dog Town.

Old Peter Prairie-Dog
Digs him a cellar
In Prairie-Dog Town,
With a ceiling that is arched
And a wall that is round,
And the earth he takes out he makes into a mound.
And the hall and the cellar
Are dark as dark,
And you can't see a spark,
Not a single spark;
And the way to them cannot be found.

Old Peter Prairie-Dog
Knows a very clever trick
Of behaving like a stick
When he hears a sudden sound,
Like an old dead stick;
And when you turn your head
He'll jump quick, quick,
And be another stick
When you look around.
It *is* a clever trick,
And it keeps him safe and sound
In the cellar and the halls
That are under the mound
In Prairie-Dog Town.

Mary Austin, *The Children Sing in the Far West*
Reprinted by permission of and arrangement with
Houghton Mifflin Company, the authorized publishers

THE JOLLY WOODCHUCK

The woodchuck's very very fat
But doesn't care a pin for that.

When nights are long and the snow is deep,
Down in his hole he lies asleep.

Under the earth is a warm little room
The drowsy woodchuck calls his home.

Rolls of fat and fur surround him,
With all his children curled around him,

Snout to snout and tail to tail.
He never awakes in the wildest gale;

When icicles snap and the north wind blows
He snores in his sleep and rubs his nose.

Marion Edey and Dorothy Grider, *Open the Door*

OPOSSUM

Have you ever in your life seen a Possum play possum?
Have you ever in your life seen a Possum play dead?
When a Possum is trapped and can't get away
He turns up his toes and lays down his head,
Bats both his eyes and rolls over dead.
But then when you leave him and run off to play,
The Possum that really was just playing possum
Gets up in a flash and scurries away.

William Jay Smith, *Boy Blue's Book of Beasts*

THE LITTLE FOX

Who came in the quiet night,
Trotting so lightly?
It was the russet fox who came
And with his shadow played a game;
Where the snow lay whitely
And the moon shone brightly
There he wrote his name.

Who spoke in the winter night,
A cold sound and lonely?
The clock-faced owl, so round and hunchy,
The yellow-eyed owl, in a voice so crunchy:
"Who-oo-oo-oo, are you?
I *like* to be only
Squat and bunchy—
Do you-oo-oo-oo, too?"

Marion Edey and Dorothy Grider, *Open the Door*
Copyright 1949 by Marion Edey and Dorothy Grider
Reprinted by permission of the publishers, Charles Scribner's Sons

NIGHT OF WIND

How lost is the little fox at the borders of night,
Poised in the forest of fern, in the trample of wind!
Caught by the blowing cold of the mountain darkness,
He shivers and runs under tall trees, whimpering,
Brushing the tangles of dew. Pausing and running,
He searches the warm and shadowy hollow, the deep
Home on the mountain's side where the nuzzling, soft
Bodies of little foxes may hide and sleep.

Frances Frost, *Pool in the Meadow*
Reprinted by permission of and arrangement with
Houghton Mifflin Company, the authorized publishers

123

LITTLE THINGS

Little things, that run, and quail,
And die, in silence and despair!

Little things, that fight, and fail,
And fall, on sea, and earth, and air!

All trapped and frightened little things,
The mouse, the coney, hear our prayer!

As we forgive those done to us,
—The lamb, the linnet, and the hare—

Forgive us all our trespasses,
Little creatures, everywhere!

James Stephens, *Collected Poems*

FIREFLY

A little light is going by,
Is going up to see the sky,
A little light with wings.

I never could have thought of it,
To have a little bug all lit
And made to go on wings.

Elizabeth Madox Roberts, *Under the Tree*

I'd like to be a worm
And squirm
In nice soft dirt,
And not have to worry
Or ever be sorry
Of getting mud on my nice clean shirt.

Zhenya Gay, *Jingle Jangle*

Fuzzy wuzzy, creepy crawly
    Caterpillar funny,
You will be a butterfly
    When the days are sunny.

Winging, flinging, dancing, springing
    Butterfly so yellow,
You were once a caterpillar,
    Wriggly, wiggly fellow.

Lillian Schulz Vanada
In *Sung under the Silver Umbrella*
The Macmillan Company, New York, 1935

BUTTERFLY

As I walked through my garden
I saw a butterfly light on a flower.
His wings were pink and purple:
He spoke a small word . . .
It was *Follow!*
"I cannot follow"
I told him,
"I have to go the opposite way."

Hilda Conkling, *Poems by a Little Girl*
Copyright 1920 by J. B. Lippincott Company

BUTTERFLY

Of living creatures most I prize
Black-spotted yellow Butterflies
Sailing softly through the skies,

Whisking light from each sunbeam,
Gliding over field and stream—
Like fans unfolding in a dream,

Like fans of gold lace flickering
Before a drowsy elfin king
For whom the thrush and linnet sing—

Soft and beautiful and bright
As hands that move to touch the light
When Mother leans to say good night.

William Jay Smith, *Boy Blue's Book of Beasts*

GREEN MOTH

The night the green moth came for me,
    A creamy moon poured down the hill,
The meadow seemed a silver sea,
Small pearls were hung in every tree,
    And all so still, so still—

He floated in on my white bed,
    A strange and soundless fellow.
I saw the horns wave on his head,
    He stepped across my pillow
In tiny ermine boots, and spread
    His cape of green and yellow.

He came so close that I could see
   His golden eyes, and sweet and chill,
His faint breath wavered over me.
"Come Child, my Beautiful," said he,
   And all so still, so still—

Winifred Welles, *Skipping Along Alone*
The Macmillan Company, New York, 1931

LITTLE SNAIL

I saw a little snail
Come down the garden walk.
He wagged his head this way . . . that way . . .
Like a clown in a circus.
He looked from side to side
As though he were from a different country.
I have always said he carries his house on his back . . .
To-day in the rain
I saw that it was his umbrella!

Hilda Conkling, *Poems by a Little Girl*
Copyright 1920 by J. B. Lippincott Company

SNAIL

Little snail,
Dreaming you go.
Weather and rose
Is all you know.

Weather and rose
Is all you see,
Drinking
The dewdrop's
Mystery.

Langston Hughes, *Fields of Wonder*
Reprinted by permission of Alfred A. Knopf, Inc.
Copyright 1947 by Langston Hughes

127

OUR
MR. TOAD

Our Mr. Toad
Has a nice abode
Under the first front step.
When it rains he's cool
In a secret pool
Where the water goes
    drip
    drop
    drep.

Our Mr. Toad
Will avoid the road:
He's a private-cellar man.
And it's not much fun
In the broiling sun
When you *have* a good
    ten
    tone
    tan.

Our Mr. Toad
Has a kind of code
That tells him the coast is clear.
Then away he'll hop
With a stop, stop, stop
When the dusk draws
    nigh
    no
    near.

David McCord, *Far and Few*
Copyright 1929, 1931, 1952 by David McCord
By permission of Little, Brown & Company, Boston

THE LITTLE TURTLE

There was a little turtle.
He lived in a box.
He swam in a puddle.
He climbed on the rocks.

He snapped at a mosquito.
He snapped at a flea.
He snapped at a minnow.
And he snapped at me.

He caught the mosquito.
He caught the flea.
He caught the minnow.
But he didn't catch me.

Vachel Lindsay, *Golden Whales*
Copyright 1920, 1948 by The Macmillan Company
and used with their permission

GRANDFATHER FROG

Fat green frog sits by the pond,
Big frog, bull frog, grandfather frog.
Croak—croak—croak.
Shuts his eye, opens his eye,
Rolls his eye, winks his eye,
Waiting for
A little fat fly.
Croak, croak.
I go walking down by the pond,
I want to see the big green frog,
I want to stare right into his eye,
Rolling, winking, funny old eye.
But oh! he hears me coming by.
Croak—croak—
SPLASH!

Louise Seaman Bechtel
In *Another Here and Now Story Book* by Lucy Sprague Mitchell
Published and copyright 1937
by E. P. Dutton & Co., Inc., New York

THE
NEWT

The little newt
Is not a brute,
A fish or fowl,
A kind of owl:
He doesn't prowl
Or run or dig
Or grow too big.
He doesn't fly
Or laugh or cry—
He doesn't try.

The little newt
Is mostly mute,
And grave and wise,
And has two eyes.
He lives inside,
Or likes to hide;
But after rain
He's out again
And rather red,
I should have said.

The little newt
Of great repute
Has legs, a tail,
A spotted veil.
He walks alone
From stone to stone,
From log to log,
From bog to bog,
From tree to tree,
From you to me.

The little newt
By grass or root
Is very kind
But hard to find.
His hands and feet
Are always neat:
They move across
The mildest moss.
He's very shy,
He's never spry—
Don't ask me why.

David McCord, *Far and Few*

THE

SILENT

SNAKE

The birds go fluttering in the air,
    The rabbits run and skip,
Brown squirrels race along the bough,
    The May-flies rise and dip;
But, whilst these creatures play and leap,
The silent snake goes *creepy-creep!*

The birdies sing and whistle loud,
    The busy insects hum,
The squirrels chat, the frogs say "Croak!"
    But the snake is always dumb.
With not a sound through grasses deep
The silent snake goes *creepy-creep!*

Unknown

THE

ANT

VILLAGE

Somebody up in the rocky pasture
    Heaved the stone over.
Here are the cells and a network of furrows
    In the roots of the clover.

Hundreds of eggs lie fitted in patterns,
    Waxy and yellow.
Hundreds of ants are racing and struggling.
    One little fellow

Shoulders an egg as big as his body,
    Ready for hatching.
Darkness is best, so everyone's rushing,
    Hastily snatching

Egg after egg to the lowest tunnels.
    And suddenly, where
Confusion had been, there now is nothing.
    Ants gone. Cells bare.

Marion Edey and Dorothy Grider, *Open the Door*

GOOD

MORNING

One day I saw a downy duck,
With feathers on his back;
I said, "Good morning, downy duck,"
And he said, "Quack, quack, quack."

One day I saw a timid mouse,
He was so shy and meek;
I said, "Good morning, timid mouse,"
And he said, "Squeak, squeak, squeak."

132

One day I saw a curly dog,
I met him with a bow;
I said, "Good morning, curly dog,"
And he said, "Bow-wow-wow."

One day I saw a scarlet bird,
He woke me from my sleep;
I said, "Good morning, scarlet bird,"
And he said, "Cheep, cheep, cheep."

Muriel Sipe (Mrs. David Ross)
In *Sung under the Silver Umbrella*
The Macmillan Company, New York, 1935
By permission of the author

THE BARNYARD

When the Farmer's day is done,
In the barnyard, ev'ry one,
Beast and bird politely say,
"Thank you for my food to-day."

The cow says, "Moo!"
The pigeon, "Coo!"
The sheep says, "Baa!"
The lamb says, "Maa!"
The hen, "Cluck! Cluck!"
"Quack!" says the duck;
The dog, "Bow Wow!"
The cat, "Meow!"
The horse says, "Neigh!
I love sweet hay!"
The pig near by,
Grunts in his sty.

When the barn is locked up tight,
Then the Farmer says, "Good night!";
Thanks his animals, ev'ry one,
For the work that has been done.

Maude Burnham

THE FAMILY
(*German*)

Widdy-widdy-wurkey
Is the name of my turkey;
There-and-back again
Is the name of my hen;
Waggle-tail-loose
Is the name of my goose;
Widdy-widdy-wurkey
Is the name of my turkey.

Widdy-widdy-wurkey
Is the name of my turkey;
Quackery-quack
Is the name of my duck;
Grummelty-grig
Is the name of my pig;
Widdy-widdy-wurkey
Is the name of my turkey.

Widdy-widdy-wurkey
Is the name of my turkey;
Tinker-Tog
Is the name of my dog;
Velvety-pat
Is the name of my cat;
Widdy-widdy-wurkey
Is the name of my turkey.

Widdy-widdy-wurkey
Is the name of my turkey;
Fiery-speed
Is the name of my steed;
Run-of-the-house
Is the name of my mouse;
Widdy-widdy-wurkey
Is the name of my turkey.

Widdy-widdy-wurkey
Is the name of my turkey;
Very-well-done
Is the name of my son;
Dearer-than-life
Is the name of my wife;
Widdy-widdy-wurkey
Is the name of my turkey.

And now you know my famil*ee*
And all that does belong to me.

In *Picture Rhymes from Foreign Lands*
Translated by Rose Fyleman
Copyright 1935 by Rose Fyleman
Reprinted by permission of J. B. Lippincott Company

Minnie and Mattie
  And fat little May,
Out in the country,
  Spending a day.

Such a bright day,
  With the sun glowing,
And the trees half in leaf,
  And the grass growing.

Pinky white pigling
  Squeals through his snout,
Woolly white lambkin
  Frisks all about.

Cluck! cluck! the nursing hen
  Summons her folk,—
Ducklings all downy soft,
  Yellow as yolk.

Cluck! cluck! the mother hen
  Summons her chickens
To peck the dainty bits
  Found in her pickings.

Minnie and Mattie
  And May carry posies,
Half of sweet violets,
  Half of primroses.

Christina Georgina Rossetti, *Sing-Song*

A son just born
To a duck is a drake,
And the child of a goose
Is called gosling,
And the moment when
The little chick steps
From the egg of a hen
A chicken is born.
But who knows the name
Of the new-born son
Of the beautiful swan?

(Cygnet)

Mary Britton Miller, *Give a Guess*
Published by Pantheon Books, Inc., New York, 1957

CHICKEN

Clapping her platter stood plump Bess,
  And all across the green
Came scampering in, on wing and claw,
  Chicken fat and lean:—
Dorking, Spaniard, Cochin China,
  Bantams sleek and small,
Like feathers blown in a great wind,
  They came at Bessie's call.

Walter de la Mare, *Collected Poems, 1901–1918*
Copyright 1920 by Henry Holt and Company, Inc.
Copyright 1948 by Walter de la Mare
Reprinted by permission of the publishers
(Also in *Rhymes and Verses* by Walter de la Mare
Published by Henry Holt and Company, Inc., New York, 1947)

CHANTICLEER

High and proud on the barnyard fence
Walks rooster in the morning.
He shakes his comb, he shakes his tail
And gives his daily warning.

"Get up, you lazy boys and girls,
It's time you should be dressing!"
I wonder if he keeps a clock,
Or if he's only guessing.

John Farrar, *Songs for Parents*
Yale University Press, New Haven, 1921

CHANTICLEER

Of all the birds from East to West
    That tuneful are and dear,
I love that farmyard bird the best,
    They call him Chanticleer.

Gold plume and copper plume,
    Comb of scarlet gay;
'Tis he that scatters night and gloom,
    And summons back the day!

He is the sun's brave herald
    Who, ringing his blithe horn,
Calls round a world dew-pearled
    The heavenly airs of morn.

138

Oh, clear gold, shrill and bold,
    He calls through creeping mist
The mountains from the night and cold
    To rose and amethyst.

He sets the birds to singing,
    And calls the flowers to rise;
The morning cometh, bringing
    Sweet sleep to heavy eyes.

Gold plume and silver plume,
    Comb of coral gay;
'Tis he packs off the night and gloom,
    And summons home the day.

Black fear he sends it flying,
    Black care he drives afar;
And creeping shadows sighing
    Before the morning star.

The birds of all the forest
    Have dear and pleasant cheer,
But yet I hold the rarest
    The farmyard Chanticleer.

Red cock and black cock,
    Gold cock or white,
The flower of all the feathered flock,
    He summons back the light!

Katherine Tynan, *Collected Poems*

Reprinted by permission of The Macmillan Company
By permission also of Miss Pamela Hinkson
and The Society of Authors

THE HENS

The night was coming very fast;
It reached the gate as I ran past.

The pigeons had gone to the tower of the church
And all the hens were on their perch,

Up in the barn, and I thought I heard
A piece of a little purring word.

I stopped inside, waiting and staying,
To try to hear what the hens were saying.

They were asking something, that was plain,
Asking it over and over again.

One of them moved and turned around,
Her feathers made a ruffled sound,

A ruffled sound, like a bushful of birds,
And she said her little asking words.

She pushed her head close into her wing,
But nothing answered anything.

Elizabeth Madox Roberts, *Under the Tree*

THE DUCKS

When our ducks waddle to the pond,
They're awkward as awkward can be—
But when they get in the water and swim,
They glide most gracefully.

Alice Wilkins
In *The Golden Flute*
The John Day Company, Inc., New York, 1932

DUCKS AT DAWN

"Quack! Quack!"
Said seven ducks at dawn
While night dew
Glimmered on the lawn.

"Quack! Quack!" they said.
"It's time to eat.
We'll go hunt mushrooms
For a treat."

And in the light
Of early dawn
I saw them chasing
On the lawn.

They sought their treat
With hungry quacks
And marked the dew
With criss-cross tracks.

They ate the mushrooms
One by one
And quacked to greet
The rising sun.

But in my bed
I settled back
And slept to tunes
Of "Quack! Quack! Quack!"

James S. Tippett, *A World to Know*
Copyright 1933 by Harper & Brothers

DUCKS' DITTY

All along the backwater,
Through the rushes tall,
Ducks are a-dabbling,
Up tails all!

Ducks' tails, drakes' tails,
Yellow feet a-quiver,
Yellow bills all out of sight
Busy in the river!

Slushy green undergrowth
Where the roach swim—
Here we keep our larder,
Cool and full and dim.

Everyone for what he likes!
We like to be
Heads down, tails up,
Dabbling free!

High in the blue above
Swifts whirl and call—
We are down a-dabbling
Up tails all!

Kenneth Grahame, *The Wind in the Willows*

QUACK!

The duck is whiter than whey is,
His tail tips up over his back,
The eye in his head is as round as a button,
And he says, *Quack! Quack!*

He swims on his bright blue mill-pond,
By the willow tree under the shack,
Then stands on his head to see down to the bottom,
And says, *Quack! Quack!*

When Mollie steps out of the kitchen,
For apron—pinned round with a sack;
He squints at her round face, her dish, and what's in it,
And says, *Quack! Quack!*

He preens the pure snow of his feathers
In the sun by the wheat-straw stack;
At dusk waddles home with his brothers and sisters,
And says, *Quack! Quack!*

Walter de la Mare, *Bells and Grass*

Copyright 1942 by Walter de la Mare
Reprinted by permission of The Viking Press, Inc., New York
By permission of the author and by Faber and Faber, Limited
(Also in *Rhymes and Verses* by Walter de la Mare
Published by Henry Holt and Company, Inc., New York, 1947)

Baa, baa, black sheep,
　　Have you any wool?
Yes, sir, yes, sir,
　　Three bags full;

One for my master,
　　One for my dame,
And one for the little boy
　　Who lives down the lane.

Mother Goose

MARY'S

LAMB

Mary had a little lamb,
　　Its fleece was white as snow;
And everywhere that Mary went
　　The lamb was sure to go.

He followed her to school one day,
　　Which was against the rule;
It made the children laugh and play
　　To see a lamb at school.

And so the teacher turned him out,
　　But still he lingered near,
And waited patiently about
　　Till Mary did appear.

"What makes the lamb love Mary so?"
　　The eager children cry.
"Oh, Mary loves the lamb, you know,"
　　The teacher did reply.

Sarah Josepha Hale

I HELD A LAMB

One day when I went visiting,
A little lamb was there,
I picked it up and held it tight,
It didn't seem to care.
Its wool was soft and felt so warm—
Like sunlight on the sand,
And when I gently put it down
It licked me on the hand.

Kim Worthington
In *Child Life*, September 1954
Copyright 1954 by Child Life, Inc.
By permission of the author

THE COW

The friendly cow all red and white,
  I love with all my heart:
She gives me cream, with all her might,
  To eat with apple-tart.

She wanders lowing here and there,
  And yet she cannot stray,
All in the pleasant open air,
  The pleasant light of day;

And blown by all the winds that pass
  And wet with all the showers,
She walks among the meadow grass
  And eats the meadow flowers.

Robert Louis Stevenson, *A Child's Garden of Verses*

145

GREEN GRASS
AND
WHITE MILK

Teeney and Weeney together are going
  Down to the dairy to fetch the milk,
  Down through the meadow as shiny as silk,
Where grass bends over and daisies are blowing.

With never a word yet somehow hobnobbing,
  Teeney and Weeney, like tots in a dream,
  Trudge solemnly down to bring back the cream,
Their bright yellow heads like buttercups bobbing.

Up through the field that the sun makes glossy,
  Tossing their tails and taking their time,
  Tinkling their bells in a rusty chime,
Cropping and crunching, come Bossy and Bossy.

They stoop to the ground or they stand unblinking,
  Munching and munching, making green grass
  Into white milk to pour into a glass
For Teeney and Weeney to have for drinking.

Winifred Welles, *Skipping Along Alone*
The Macmillan Company, New York, 1931

BUTTERCUP COW

Buttercup Cow has milk for me
I drink in my silver cup at tea.
Buttercup Cow is speckled and white,
She lives in the meadow from morning till night.

Buttercup Cow hasn't got any bed,
But the moon and the stars look in at her shed.
Buttercup Cow, I'm glad to be me,
Drinking your pretty white milk for my tea.

Elizabeth Rendall

In "Here We Come A' Piping," Book I (Compiled by Rose Fyleman)
By permission of Basil Blackwell & Mott, Ltd., Oxford

OUR LITTLE CALF

Our little calf is woollier.
Inside her ears is soft with fur.
She isn't playful any more.

She used to kick her little heels
And run across the summer fields.

Now all she does is stand and stare
Across the stubble, wondering where
Her good grass dinner's gone and why
That *white* is falling from the sky.

You silly thing, it's winter now.
What you are looking at is snow.

But spring will come and summer too.

And when the world is warm again
And fields are green, d'you know what then?
You'll be our cow!

Dorothy Aldis, *All Together*

Copyright 1925, 1952 by Dorothy Aldis
By permission of G. P. Putnam's Sons, New York

147

THE
NEW
BABY
CALF

Buttercup, the cow, had a new baby calf,
               a fine baby calf,
                     a strong baby calf,
Not strong like his mother
But strong for a calf,
For *this* baby calf was so *new!*

Buttercup licked him with her strong warm tongue,
Buttercup washed him with her strong warm tongue,
Buttercup brushed him with her strong warm tongue,
   And the new baby calf *liked that!*

The new baby calf took a very little walk,
               a tiny little walk,
                     a teeny little walk,
But his long legs wobbled
When he took a little walk,
   And the new baby calf fell down.

Buttercup told him with a low soft "Moo-oo!"
That he was doing very well for one so very new
And she talked very gently, as mother cows do,
   And the new baby calf *liked that!*

The new baby calf took another little walk,
        a little longer walk,
          a little stronger walk,
He walked around his mother and he found the place to drink.
    And the new baby calf liked *that!*

Buttercup told him with another low moo
That drinking milk from mother was a fine thing to do,
That she had lots of milk for him and for the farmer too,
    And the new baby calf liked *that!*

The new baby calf drank milk every day,
His legs grew so strong that he could run and play,
He learned to eat grass and then grain and hay,
    And the big baby calf grew fat!

Edith H. Newlin
In *Very Young Verses*
Houghton Mifflin Company, Boston, 1945
By permission of the author

THE

PASTURE

I'm going out to clean the pasture spring;
I'll only stop to rake the leaves away
(And wait to watch the water clear, I may):
I sha'n't be gone long.—You come too.

I'm going out to fetch the little calf
That's standing by the mother. It's so young
It totters when she licks it with her tongue.
I sha'n't be gone long.—You come too.

Robert Frost, *Collected Poems of Robert Frost*
Copyright 1930, 1939 by Henry Holt and Company, Inc.
Copyright 1939 by Robert Frost
Reprinted by permission of Henry Holt and Company, Inc.

THE YOUNG CALVES

A hush had fallen on the birds,
   And it was almost night,
When I came round a turn and saw
   A whole year's loveliest sight.

Two calves that thought their month of life
   Meant June through all the year
Were coming down the grassy road
   As slender as young deer.

They stopped amazed and took me in,
   Putting their ears out far,
And in each of four round eyes
   There was an evening star.

They did not breathe, they stared so hard,
   Brother close to brother,
Then their legs awoke, and they
   Turned flank to flank for mother.

A small boy in torn knickers came
   And caught them as they fled,
He put a slender arm around
   Each slender, startled head.

He never looked at me at all,
   I was not in his mind;
The three of them went down the road
   And never glanced behind.

Robert P. Tristram Coffin, *Saltwater Farm*

DAPPLE-GRAY

I had a little pony,
    His name was Dapple-gray,
I lent him to a lady,
    To ride a mile away;

She whipped him, she slashed him,
    She rode him through the mire;
I would not lend my pony now
    For all the lady's hire.

Mother Goose

 This is the way the ladies ride,
    Tri, tre, tre, tree,
    Tri, tre, tre, tree!
This is the way the ladies ride,
    Tri, tre, tre, tre, tri-tre-tre-tree!

This is the way the gentlemen ride,
    Gallop-a-trot,
    Gallop-a-trot!
This is the way the gentlemen ride,
    Gallop-a-gallop-a-trot!

This is the way the farmers ride,
    Hobbledy-hoy,
    Hobbledy-hoy!
This is the way the farmers ride,
    Hobbledy-hobbledy-hoy!

Mother Goose

HORSE

His bridle hung around the post;
The sun and the leaves made spots come down;
I looked close at him through the fence;
The post was drab and he was brown.

His nose was long and hard and still,
And on his lip were specks like chalk.
But once he opened up his eyes,
And he began to talk.

He didn't talk out with his mouth;
He didn't talk with words or noise.
The talk was there along his nose;
It seemed and then it was.

He said the day was hot and slow,
And he said he didn't like the flies;
They made him have to shake his skin,
And they got drowned in his eyes.

He said that drab was just about
The same as brown, but he was not
A post, he said, to hold a fence.
"I'm horse," he said, "that's what!"

And then he shut his eyes again.
As still as they had been before.
He said for me to run along
And not to bother him any more.

Elizabeth Madox Roberts, *Under the Tree*
Copyright 1922 by B. W. Huebsch, Inc., 1950 by Ivor S. Roberts
By permission of The Viking Press, Inc., New York

TROT ALONG, PONY

Trot along, pony.
   Late in the day,
Down by the meadow
   Is the loveliest way.

The apples are rosy
   And ready to fall.
The branches hang over
   By Grandfather's wall.

But the red sun is sinking
   Away out of sight.
The chickens are settling
   Themselves for the night.

Your stable is waiting
   And supper will come.
So turn again, pony,
   Turn again home.

Marion Edey and Dorothy Grider, *Open the Door*

THE

RUNAWAY

Once, when the snow of the year was beginning to fall,
We stopped by a mountain pasture to say, "Whose colt?"
A little Morgan had one forefoot on the wall,
The other curled at his breast. He dipped his head
And snorted to us. And then he had to bolt.
We heard the miniature thunder where he fled
And we saw him or thought we saw him dim and gray,
Like a shadow against the curtain of falling flakes.
"I think the little fellow's afraid of the snow.
He isn't winter-broken. It isn't play
With the little fellow at all. He's running away.
I doubt if even his mother could tell him, 'Sakes,
It's only weather.' He'd think she didn't know!
Where is his mother? He can't be out alone."
And now he comes again with a clatter of stone,
And mounts the wall again with whited eyes
And all his tail that isn't hair up straight.
He shudders his coat as if to throw off flies.
"Whoever it is that leaves him out so late,
When other creatures have gone to stall and bin,
Ought to be told to come and take him in."

Robert Frost, *New Hampshire*

EXCUSE US, ANIMALS IN THE ZOO

Excuse us, Animals in the Zoo,
I'm sure we're very rude to you;
Into your private house we stare
And never ask you if you care;
And never ask you if you mind.
Perhaps we really are not kind;
I think it must be hard to stay
And have folks looking in all day,
I wouldn't like my house that way.

Excuse us, Animals in the Zoo,
I'm sure we're very rude to you;
Suppose you all to our house came
And stared at us and called our name.
I hardly think we'd like it at all
In a house that didn't have a wall.
No wonder you pace up and down the floor
And growl a little or even roar—
I'm sure if 'twere we, we'd growl much more.

Excuse us, Animals in the Zoo,
I'm sure we're very rude to you.

Annette Wynne, *All Through the Year*

THE ELEPHANT'S TRUNK

The elephant always carries his trunk.
I couldn't do that with my own.
His trunk is a part of himself, you see—
It's part of his head—it's grown!

Alice Wilkins
In *The Golden Flute*
The John Day Company, Inc., New York, 1932

155

THE ELEPHANT

When people call this beast to mind,
   They marvel more and more
At such a *little* tail behind,
   So LARGE a trunk before.

Hilaire Belloc, *Cautionary Verses*
Reprinted by permission of Alfred A. Knopf, Inc.
Copyright 1931 by Hilaire Belloc

THE ELEPHANT

Here comes the elephant
Swaying along
With his cargo of children
All singing a song:
To the tinkle of laughter
He goes on his way,
And his cargo of children
Have crowned him with may.
His legs are in leather
And padded his toes:
He can root up an oak
With a whisk of his nose:
With a wave of his trunk
And a turn of his chin
He can pull down a house,
Or pick up a pin.
Beneath his gray forehead
A little eye peers;
Of what is he thinking
Between those wide ears?
Of what does he think?
If he wished to tease,
He could twirl his keeper
Over the trees:

If he were not kind,
He could play cup and ball
With Robert and Helen,
And Uncle Paul:
But that gray forehead,
Those crinkled ears,
Have learned to be kind
In a hundred years:
And so with the children
He goes on his way
To the tinkle of laughter
And crowned with the may.

Herbert Asquith, *Pillicock Hill*
Reprinted by permission of The Macmillan Company
By permission also of the author and William Heinemann, Ltd.

THE MONKEYS

Sing a song of monkeys,
A jolly bunch of monkeys!
Leaping, swinging in their cages
Looking wise as ancient sages,
Nonchalant and carefree manner,
Nibbling peanut or banana,
Every day is just another
To a monkey or his brother.

Sing a song of monkeys,
Happy, merry monkeys,
If you're ever tired or blue
I can tell you what to do!
Let the monkeys at the Zoo
Make a monkey out of you!

In *St. Nicholas*, February 1936
By permission of Juliet Lit Stern

**HERE
SHE IS**

Jungle necklaces are hung
Around her tiger throat
And on her tiger arms are slung
Bracelets black and brown;
She shows off when she lies down
All her tiger strength and grace,
You can see the tiger blaze
In her tiger eyes, her tiger face.

Mary Britton Miller, *Give a Guess*
Published by Pantheon Books, Inc., New York, 1957

CAMEL

O camel in the zoo,
You don't do any of the things
They tell me that you used to do
In Egypt, and in other lands,
Carrying potentates and kings
Across the burning desert sands
With gorgeous trappings made of blue
And scarlet silks to cover you.

Your humps are carried on your back
Just the way they always were,
You thrust your old head up and back,
And make your neck go in and out,
And spill the foam upon your fur,
And writhe and jerk and rear about,
But kneel no more upon the sands
To mount the kings of Eastern lands.

Mary Britton Miller, *Menagerie*
Published by The Macmillan Company, New York, 1928
By permission of the author

THE HIPPOPOTAMUS

In the squdgy river,
Down the oozely bank,
Where the ripples shiver,
And the reeds are rank—

Where the purple Kippo
Makes an awful fuss,
Lives the hip-hip-hippo
Hippo-pot-a-mus!

Broad his back and steady;
Broad and flat his nose;
Sharp and keen and ready
Little eyes are those.

You would think him dreaming
Where the mud is deep.
It is only seeming—
He is not asleep.

Better not disturb him,
There'd be an awful fuss
If you touched the Hippo,
Hippo-pot-a-mus.

Georgia Roberts Durston

In *Junior Home Magazine*
By permission of Child Training Association, Incorporated,
publishers of *Children's Activities*

THE PERFORMING SEAL

Who is so proud
As not to feel
A secret awe
Before a seal
That keeps such sleek
And wet repose
While twirling candles
On his nose?

Rachel Field, *Poems*

SEAL LULLABY

Oh! hush thee, my baby, the night is behind us,
And black are the waters that sparkled so green.
The moon, o'er the combers, looks downward to find us
At rest in the hollows that rustle between.
Where billow meets billow, then soft be thy pillow,
Ah, weary wee flipperling, curl at thy ease!
The storm shall not wake thee, nor shark overtake thee,
Asleep in the arms of the slow-swinging seas!

Rudyard Kipling, *The Jungle Book*

160

TRAVELING WE GO

Jog on, jog on, the foot-path way,
 And merrily hent the stile-a:
A merry heart goes all the day,
 Your sad tires in a mile-a.

A MODERN DRAGON

A train is a dragon that roars through the dark.
He wriggles his tail as he sends up a spark.
He pierces the night with his one yellow eye,
And all the earth trembles when he rushes by.

Rowena Bennett, *Songs from Around a Toadstool Table*
Follett Publishing Company, Chicago, 1930

THE BABY GOES TO BOSTON

What does the train say?
  Jiggle joggle, jiggle joggle!
What does the train say?
  Jiggle joggle jee!
Will the little baby go
Riding with the locomo?
Loky moky poky stoky
  Smoky choky chee!

Ting! ting! the bells ring,
  Jiggle joggle, jiggle joggle!
Ting! ting! the bells ring,
  Jiggle joggle jee!
Ring for joy because we go
Riding with the locomo,
Loky moky poky stoky
  Smoky choky chee!

Look! how the trees run,
    Jiggle joggle, jiggle joggle!
Each chasing t' other one,
    Jiggle joggle jee!
Are they running for to go
Riding with the locomo?
Loky moky poky stoky
    Smoky choky chee!

Over the hills now,
    Jiggle joggle, jiggle joggle!
Down through the vale below,
    Jiggle joggle jee!
All the cows and horses run,
Crying, "Won't you take us on,
Loky moky poky stoky
    Smoky choky chee?"

So, so, the miles go,
    Jiggle joggle, jiggle joggle!
Now it's fast and now it's slow,
    Jiggle joggle jee!
When we're at our journey's end,
Say good-by to snorting friend,
Loky moky poky stoky
    Smoky choky chee!

Laura E. Richards, *Tirra Lirra*
Little, Brown & Company, Boston, 1932

163

TEXAS
TRAINS AND
TRAILS

Whenever I ride on the Texas plains
I never hear the couplings cluck,
I never hear the trains
Go chuck-a-luck, chuck-a-luck, chuck-a-luck,
I never hear the engine snort and snuffle,
I never see the smoke plume, I never watch the rails,
But I see the moving dust where the beef herds shuffle,
And I think I am a cowboy,
A rope and tie 'em cowboy,
Punching Texas longhorns
On the Texas trails.

And the engine goes *Whoop!*
Whoopee, whoopala!
And the cars go *Ki-yi,*
Ki-yi, ki-yi, coma-la ky-yi,
              Whoopala,
Ki-yi!
          Whoop!

No, I never hear the bell, nor the brakeman call
When I ride on the Texas trains;
But I hear the steers bellow and the yearlings bawl,
And the lone wolf howl on the wire grass plains.
And I never play I'm fireman, nor anything like that,
For I'm playing I'm a cowboy,
A bronco-bustin' cowboy,
Riding Texas longhorns
In a ten-gallon hat.

And the trains go *Youpi-ya,*
Get a-long, dogies,
Get a-long, get a-long
Youpi-yi, youpi-ya,
Youpi-youpi-youpi-ya
Get a-long, get a-long,
Youpi-ya,
　　　　Yo-o-u-u-p!

Mary Austin, *The Children Sing in the Far West*
Reprinted by permission of and arrangement with
Houghton Mifflin Company, the authorized publishers

FROM

A

RAILWAY

CARRIAGE

Faster than fairies, faster than witches,
Bridges and houses, hedges and ditches;
And charging along like troops in a battle
All through the meadows the horses and cattle:
All of the sights of the hill and the plain
Fly as thick as driving rain;
And ever again, in the wink of an eye,
Painted stations whistle by.

Here is a child who clambers and scrambles,
All by himself and gathering brambles;
Here is a tramp who stands and gazes;
And there is the green for stringing the daisies!
Here is a cart run away in the road
Lumping along with man and load;
And here is a mill, and there is a river:
Each a glimpse and gone for ever!

Robert Louis Stevenson, *A Child's Garden of Verses*

165

TRAINS

Over the mountains,
Over the plains,
Over the rivers,
Here come the trains.

Carrying passengers,
Carrying mail,
Bringing their precious loads
In without fail.

Thousands of freight cars
All rushing on
Through day and darkness,
Through dusk and dawn.

Over the mountains,
Over the plains,
Over the rivers,
Here come the trains.

James S. Tippett, *I Go A-Traveling*

TRAINS AT NIGHT

I like the whistle of trains at night,
The fast trains thundering by so proud!
They rush and rumble across the world,
They ring wild bells and they toot so loud!

But I love better the slower trains.
They take their time through the world instead,
And whistle softly and stop to tuck
Each sleepy blinking town in bed!

Frances Frost, *The Packet*

166

THE WAYS OF TRAINS

I hear the engine pounding
in triumph down the track—
trains take away the ones you love
and then they bring them back!

trains take away the ones you love
to worlds both strange and new
and then, with care and courtesy,
they bring them back to you.

The engine halts and snuffs and snorts,
it breathes forth smoke and fire,
then snatches crowded strangers on—
but leaves what you desire!

Elizabeth Coatsworth, *Summer Green*

TRAVEL

The railroad track is miles away,
    And the day is loud with voices speaking,
Yet there isn't a train goes by all day
    But I hear its whistle shrieking.

All night there isn't a train goes by,
    Though the night is still for sleep and dreaming
But I see its cinders red on the sky,
    And hear its engine steaming.

My heart is warm with the friends I make,
    And better friends I'll not be knowing,
Yet there isn't a train I wouldn't take,
    No matter where it's going.

Edna St. Vincent Millay, *Second April*

167

UP

IN THE

AIR

Zooming across the sky,
Like a great bird you fly,
    Airplane,
    Silvery white
    In the light.

Turning and twisting in air,
When shall I ever be there,
    Airplane,
    Piloting you
    Far in the blue?

James S. Tippett, *I Go A-Traveling*
Copyright 1929 by Harper & Brothers

TAKING

OFF

The airplane taxis down the field
And heads into the breeze,
It lifts its wheels above the ground,
It skims above the trees,
It rises high and higher
Away up toward the sun,
It's just a speck against the sky
—And now it's gone!

Unknown

Reprinted from *Very Young Verses*
Published by Houghton Mifflin Company
The editors of this book searched diligently to find the source
and to obtain permission to use this poem, but without success

AEROPLANE

There's a humming in the sky
There's a shining in the sky
Silver wings are flashing by
Silver wings are shining by
Aeroplane
Aeroplane
Flying—high

Silver wings are shining
As it goes gliding by
First it zooms
And it booms
Then it buzzes in the sky
Then its song is just a drumming
A soft little humming
Strumming
Strumming

The wings are very little things
The silver shine is gone
Just a little black speck
Away down the sky
With a soft little strumming
And a far-away humming
Aeroplane
Aeroplane
Gone—by.

Mary McB. Green

In *Another Here and Now Story Book*, by Lucy Sprague Mitchell
Published and copyright 1937
by E. P. Dutton & Co., Inc., New York

SILVER SHIPS

There are trails that a lad may follow
  When the years of his boyhood slip,
But I shall soar like a swallow
  On the wings of a silver ship,

Guiding my bird of metal,
  One with her throbbing frame,
Floating down like a petal,
  Roaring up like a flame;

Winding the wind that scatters
  Smoke from the chimney's lip,
Tearing the clouds to tatters
  With the wings of a silver ship;

Grazing the broad blue sky light
  Up where the falcons fare,
Riding the realms of twilight,
  Brushed by a comet's hair;

Snug in my coat of leather,
  Watching the skyline swing,
Shedding the world like a feather
  From the tip of a tilted wing.

There are trails that a lad may travel
  When the years of his boyhood wane,
But I'll let a rainbow ravel
  Through the wings of my silver plane.

Mildred Plew Meigs

In *Child Life*, May 1930
Copyright 1930 by Rand McNally & Company
By permission of Marion Plew Ruckel

COCKPIT IN THE CLOUDS

Two thousand feet beneath our wheels
The city sprawls across the land
Like heaps of children's blocks outflung,
In tantrums, by a giant hand.
To east a silver spire soars
And seeks to pierce our lower wing.
Above its grasp we drift along,
A tiny, droning, shiny thing.

The noon crowds pack the narrow streets.
The el trains move so slow, so slow.
Amidst their traffic, chaos, life,
The city's busy millions go.
Up here, aloof, we watch them crawl.
In crystal air we seem to poise
Behind our motor's throaty roar—
Down there, we're just another noise.

In *The* (New York) *Sun*
By permission of the author

NIGHT PLANE

The midnight plane with its riding lights
looks like a footloose star
wandering west through the blue-black night
to where the mountains are,

a star that's journeyed nearer earth
to tell each quiet farm
and little town, "Put out your lights,
children of earth. Sleep warm."

In the *New York Herald Tribune,* May 1956
By permission of the author

TO BEACHEY, 1912

Riding against the east,
A veering, steady shadow
Purrs the motor-call
Of the man-bird
Ready with the death-laughter
In his throat
And in his heart always
The love of the big blue beyond.

Only a man,
A far fleck of shadow on the east
Sitting at ease
With his hands on a wheel
And around him the large gray wings.
Hold him, great soft wings,
Keep and deal kindly, O wings,
With the cool, calm shadow at the wheel.

Carl Sandburg, *Chicago Poems*
Copyright 1916 by Henry Holt and Company, Inc.
Copyright 1944 by Carl Sandburg
Used by permission of the publishers

BOATS

The steamboat is a slow poke,
　You simply cannot rush him.
The sailboat will not move at all
　Without a wind to push him;

But the speed boat, with his sharp red nose,
　Is quite a different kind;
He tosses high the spray and leaves
　The other boats behind.

Rowena Bennett, *Songs from Around a Toadstool Table*
Follett Publishing Company, Chicago, 1930

172

FERRY-BOATS

Over the river,
Over the bay,
Ferry-boats travel
Every day.

Most of the people
Crowd to the side
Just to enjoy
Their ferry-boat ride.

Watching the seagulls,
Laughing with friends,
I'm always sorry
When the ride ends.

James S. Tippett, *I Go A-Traveling*
Copyright 1929 by Harper & Brothers

WHISTLES

I never even hear
The boats that pass by day;
By night they seem so near,
A-whistling down the bay,
That I can almost understand
The things their whistles say.

I've waked sometimes all warm
In my bed, when eerily
I have heard them out of the dark
A-whistling cheerily
To tell the sleepy folk on land
All's well at sea.

Rachel Field, *The Pointed People*
The Macmillan Company, New York, 1930

A SEA-SONG FROM THE SHORE

Hail! Ho!
Sail! Ho!
Ahoy! Ahoy! Ahoy!
Who calls to me,
So far at sea?
Only a little boy!

Sail! Ho!
Hail! Ho!
The sailor he sails the sea:
I wish he would capture
A little sea-horse
And send him home to me.

I wish, as he sails
Through the tropical gales,
He would catch me a sea-bird, too,
With its silver wings
And the song it sings,
And its breast of down and dew!

I wish he would catch me
A little mermaid,
Some island where he lands,
With her dripping curls,
And her crown of pearls,
And the looking-glass in her hands!

Hail! Ho!
Sail! Ho!
Sail far o'er the fabulous main!
And if I were a sailor,
I'd sail with you,
Though I never sailed back again.

James Whitcomb Riley, *Poems Here at Home*

174

A WET SHEET AND A FLOWING SEA

A wet sheet and a flowing sea,
  A wind that follows fast
And fills the white and rustling sail,
  And bends the gallant mast!
And bends the gallant mast, my boys,
  While, like the eagle free,
Away the good ship flies, and leaves
  Old England on the lee.

O for a soft and gentle wind!
  I heard a fair one cry;
But give to me the swelling breeze,
  And white waves heaving high:
The white waves heaving high, my lads,
  The good ship tight and free;
The world of waters is our home,
  And merry men are we.

There's tempest in yon horned moon,
  And lightning in yon cloud;
And hark the music, mariners!
  The wind is wakening loud.
The wind is wakening loud, my boys,
  The lightning flashes free—
The hollow oak our palace is,
  Our heritage the sea.

Allan Cunningham

175

SEA-FEVER

I must go down to the seas again, to the lonely sea and the sky,
And all I ask is a tall ship and a star to steer her by,
And the wheel's kick and the wind's song and the white sail's shaking
And a gray mist on the sea's face and a gray dawn breaking.

I must go down to the seas again, for the call of the running tide
Is a wild call and a clear call that may not be denied;
And all I ask is a windy day with the white clouds flying,
And the flung spray and the blown spume, and the sea-gulls crying.

I must go down to the seas again to the vagrant gypsy life
To the gull's way and the whale's way where the wind's like a whetted
    knife;
And all I ask is a merry yarn from a laughing fellow-rover,
And quiet sleep and a sweet dream when the long trick's over.

John Masefield, Story of a Round House

A horse would tire,
But I, I do not tire.
A stag would turn,
But I still keep my course.
A bird must rest,
And ashes follow fire,
But I excel
Flame, bird, or deer, or horse.

Only the wind
Do I require for ration,
Only the waves
Beneath my forefoot curled.

Eager I run
From nation unto nation
And seek my harbor
Halfway round the world.

TAXIS

Ho, for taxis green or blue,
  Hi, for taxis red,
They roll along the Avenue
  Like spools of colored thread!

Jack-o'-Lantern yellow,
Orange as the moon,
Greener than the greenest grass
Ever grew in June.
Gayly striped or checked in squares,
Wheels that twinkle bright,
Don't you think that taxis make
A very pleasant sight?
Taxis shiny in the rain,
Scudding through the snow,
Taxis flashing back the sun
Waiting in a row.

Ho, for taxis red and green,
  Hi, for taxis blue,
I wouldn't be a private car
  In sober black, would you?

STOP—GO

Automobiles
In
  a
    row
Wait to go
While the signal says:
             STOP

Bells ring
Tingaling
Red light's gone!
Green light's on!
Horns blow!
And the row
Starts
    to

          GO

Dorothy Baruch, *I Like Automobiles*
The John Day Company, New York, 1931
Copyright 1931 by Dorothy Walter Baruch

MOTOR CARS

From a city window, 'way up high,
I like to watch the cars go by.
They look like burnished beetles, black,
That leave a little muddy track
Behind them as they slowly crawl.

Sometimes they do not move at all
But huddle close with hum and drone
As though they feared to be alone.
They grope their way through fog and night
With the golden feelers of their light.

Rowena Bennett, *Songs from Around a Toadstool Table*
Follett Publishing Company, Chicago, 1930

178

SONG FOR A BLUE ROADSTER

Fly, Roadster, fly!
  The sun is high,
Gold are the fields
  We hurry by,
Green are the woods
  As we slide through,
Past harbor and headland,
  Blue on blue.

Fly, Roadster, fly!
  The hay smells sweet,
And the flowers fringing
  Each village street,
Where carts are blue,
  And barns are red,
And the road unwinds
  Like a twist of thread.

Fly, Roadster, fly!
  Leave Time behind;
Out of sight
  Shall be out of mind.
Shine and shadow,
  Blue sea, green bough,
Nothing is real
  But Here and Now.

Rachel Field, *Poems*
Copyright © 1957 by The Macmillan Company, New York
and used with their permission

COUNTRY TRUCKS

Big trucks with apples
    And big trucks with grapes
Thundering through the mountains
    While every wild thing gapes.

Thundering through the valley,
    Like something just let loose,
Big trucks with oranges
    For city children's juice.

Big trucks with peaches,
    And big trucks with pears,
Frightening all the rabbits
    And giving squirrels gray hairs.

Yet, when city children
    Sit down to plum or prune,
They know more trucks are coming
    As surely as the moon.

Monica Shannon, *Goose Grass Rhymes*

B's the Bus,
The bouncing Bus,
    That bears a shopper store-ward.
It's fun to sit
In back of it
    But seats are better forward.
Although it's big as buildings are
    And looks both bold and grand,
It has to stop obligingly
    If you but raise your hand.

Phyllis McGinley, *All Around the Town*

E is the Escalator
  That gives an elegant ride.
You step on the stair
With an easy air
  And up and up you glide.
It's nicer than scaling ladders
  Or scrambling 'round a hill,
For you climb and climb
But all the time
  You're really standing still.

Phyllis McGinley, *All Around the Town*

RUDOLPH

IS TIRED OF

THE CITY

These buildings are too close to me.
I'd like to PUSH away.
I'd like to live in the country,
And spread my arms all day.

I'd like to spread my breath out, too—
As farmers' sons and daughters do.

I'd tend the cows and chickens.
I'd do the other chores.
Then, all the hours left I'd go
A-SPREADING out-of-doors.

Gwendolyn Brooks, *Bronzeville Boys and Girls*

THE BOOKWORM

"I'm tired—oh, tired of books," said Jack,
  "I long for meadows green,
And woods where shadowy violets
  Nod their cool leaves between;
I long to see the ploughman stride
  His darkening acres o'er,
To hear the hoarse sea-waters drive
  Their billows 'gainst the shore;
I long to watch the sea-mew wheel
  Back to her rock-perched mate;
Or, where the breathing cows are housed,
  Lean, dreaming, at the gate.
Something has gone, and ink and print
  Will never bring it back;
I long for the green fields again,
  I'm tired of books," said Jack.

Walter de la Mare, *Rhymes and Verses*
Published by Henry Holt & Company, Inc., New York, 1947
By permission of the literary trustees of Walter de la Mare
and The Society of Authors, London, as their representatives

MOVING

I like to move. There's such a feeling
Of hurrying
  and scurrying,
And such a feeling
Of men with trunks and packing cases,
Of kitchen clocks and mother's laces,
Dusters, dishes, books and vases,
Toys and pans and candles.

I always find things I'd forgotten,
An old brown Teddy stuffed with cotton,
Some croquet mallets without handles,
A marble and my worn-out sandals,
A half an engine and a hat . . .
And I like that.

I like to watch the big vans backing,
And the lumbering
    and the cumbering,
And the hammering and the tacking.
I even like the packing!

And that will prove
I like to move!

Eunice Tietjens
In *Child Life*, May 1934
Copyright 1934 by Rand McNally & Company
By permission of the Estate of the author

CITY STREETS AND COUNTRY ROADS

The city has streets—
    But the country has roads.
In the country one meets
    Blue carts with their loads
Of sweet-smelling hay,
    And mangolds, and grain:
Oh, take me away
    To the country again!

In the city one sees,
    Big trams rattle by,
And the breath of the chimneys
    That blot out the sky,
And all down the pavements
    Stiff lamp-posts one sees—
But the country has hedgerows,
    The country has trees.

As sweet as the sun
    In the country is rain:
Oh, take me away
    To the country again!

Eleanor Farjeon, *Joan's Door*
Copyright 1926 by J. B. Lippincott Company
(Also in *Poems for Children* by Eleanor Farjeon
Published by J. B. Lippincott Company, Philadelphia and New York
Copyright 1951 by Eleanor Farjeon)

ROADS

A road might lead to anywhere—
  To harbor towns and quays,
Or to a witch's pointed house
  Hidden by bristly trees.
It might lead past the tailor's door,
  Where he sews with needle and thread,
Or by Miss Pim the milliner's,
  With her hats for every head.
It might be a road to a great, dark cave
  With treasure and gold piled high,
Or a road with a mountain tied to its end,
  Blue-humped against the sky.
Oh, a road might lead you anywhere—
  To Mexico or Maine.
But then, it might just fool you, and—
  Lead you back home again!

Rachel Field, *The Pointed People*
The Macmillan Company, New York, 1930

THE

LITTLE

ROAD

A little road was straying
  Across a little hill.
I asked, "May I go with you, Road?"
  It answered, "If you will."
'Twas travel-stained and shabby,
  And dust was on its face.
Said I: "How fine to wander free
  To every lovely place!

"Or if you're off to mountains
   Or if you're off to sea,
Or if you're bound across the world,
   It's all the same to me."

We loitered in the sunlight,
   We journeyed on together;
The sky was like a bluebird's wing,
   The wind was like a feather.

We passed a ruddy robin
   Who called, "How do you do?"
Some daisies shook their bonnets back
   And begged, "Ah, take us too!"

A squirrel briefly joined us,
   A brook came hurrying down;
We wandered through a meadow green
   And by a busy town.

When dusky twilight met us,
   No feet so slow as mine.
"Why, there's a little house," I said,
   "With windows all ashine.

"Perhaps, since night is nearing,
   I'd rather rest than roam."
"I knew you would," said Little Road;
   "That's why I brought you home."

Nancy Byrd Turner, *Magpie Lane*

ROADS

GO EVER

EVER ON

Roads go ever ever on,
    Over rock and under tree,
By caves where never sun has shone,
    By streams that never find the sea;
Over snow by winter sown,
    And through the merry flowers of June,
Over grass and over stone,
    And under mountains in the moon.

J. R. R. Tolkien, *The Hobbit*

Published by George Allen and Unwin, London, 1937
and Houghton Mifflin Company, Boston, 1938

And now you live dispersed on ribbon roads,
And no man knows or cares who is his neighbour
Unless his neighbour makes too much disturbance,
But all dash to and fro in motor cars,
Familiar with the roads and settled nowhere.

T. S. Eliot, from "The Rock," in *Collected Poems*

Harcourt, Brace and Company, New York, Copyright 1936
Reprinted by permission of Harcourt, Brace and Company
and Faber and Faber, Limited

FAREWELL

TO

THE FARM

The coach is at the door at last;
The eager children, mounting fast
And kissing hands, in chorus sing:
Good-bye, good-bye, to everything!

To house and garden, field and lawn,
The meadow-gates we swung upon,
To pump and stable, tree and swing,
Good-bye, good-bye, to everything!

And fare you well for evermore,
O ladder at the hayloft door,
O hayloft where the cobwebs cling,
Good-bye, good-bye, to everything!

Crack goes the whip, and off we go;
The trees and houses smaller grow;
Last, round the woody turn we swing:
Good-bye, good-bye, to everything!

Robert Louis Stevenson, *A Child's Garden of Verses*

JOHNNY FIFE AND JOHNNY'S WIFE

Oh, Johnny Fife and Johnny's wife,
　　To save their toes and heels,
They built themselves a little house
　　That ran on rolling wheels.

They hung their parrot at the door
　　Upon a painted ring,
And round and round the world they went
　　And never missed a thing;

And when they wished to eat they ate,
　　And after they had fed,
They crawled beneath a crazy quilt
　　And gayly went to bed;

And what they cared to keep they kept,
　　And what they both did not,
They poked beneath a picket fence
　　And quietly forgot.

Oh, Johnny Fife and Johnny's wife,
　　They took their brush and comb,
And round and round the world they went
　　And also stayed at home.

Mildred Plew Meigs
In *Child Life*, May 1929
Copyright 1929 by Rand McNally & Company
By permission of Marion Plew Ruckel

ADVENTURE

It's not very far to the edge of town
Where trees look up and hills look down,
We go there almost every day
To climb and swing and paddle and play.

188

It's not very far to the edge of town,
Just up one little hill and down,
And through one gate, and over two stiles—
But coming home it's miles and miles.

Harry Behn, *The Little Hill*

Afoot and light-hearted, I take to the open road,
Healthy, free, the world before me,
The long brown path before me, leading wherever I choose.

Henceforth I ask not good-fortune, I myself am good-fortune,
Henceforth I whimper no more, postpone no more, need nothing,
Done with indoor complaints, libraries, querulous criticisms,
Strong and content, I travel the open road.

Walt Whitman

Hie away, hie away,
Over bank and over brae,
Where the copsewood is the greenest,
Where the fountains glisten sheenest,
Where the lady fern grows strongest,
Where the morning dew lies longest,
Where the black-cock sweetest sips it,
Where the fairy latest trips it.
Hie to haunts right seldom seen,
Lovely, lonesome, cool, and green,
Over bank and over brae,
Hie away, hie away.

Sir Walter Scott

189

RING AROUND THE WORLD

Ring around the world
Taking hands together
All across the temperate
And the torrid weather.
Past the royal palm-trees
By the ocean sand
Make a ring around the world
Taking each other's hand;
In the valleys, on the hill,
Over the prairie spaces,
There's a ring around the world
Made of children's friendly faces.

Annette Wynne, *All Through the Year*
Copyright 1932 by Annette Wynne
Reprinted by permission of J. B. Lippincott Company

TRAVEL

I should like to rise and go
Where the golden apples grow;—
Where below another sky
Parrot islands anchored lie,
And, watched by cockatoos and goats,
Lonely Crusoes building boats;—
Where in sunshine reaching out
Eastern cities, miles about,
Are with mosque and minaret
Among sandy gardens set,
And the rich goods from near and far
Hang for sale in the bazaar;—
Where the Great Wall round China goes,
And on one side the desert blows,
And with bell and voice and drum,
Cities on the other hum;—

Where are forests, hot as fire,
Wide as England, tall as a spire,
Full of apes and cocoa-nuts
And the Negro hunters' huts;—
Where the knotty crocodile
Lies and blinks in the Nile,
And the red flamingo flies
Hunting fish before his eyes;—
Where in jungles, near and far,
Man-devouring tigers are,
Lying close and giving ear
Lest the hunt be drawing near,
Or a comer-by be seen
Swinging in a palanquin;—
Where among the desert sands
Some deserted city stands,
All its children, sweep and prince,
Grown to manhood ages since,
Not a foot in street or house,
Not a stir of child or mouse,
And when kindly falls the night,
In all the town no spark of light.
There I'll come when I'm a man
With a camel caravan;
Light a fire in the gloom
Of some dusty dining-room;
See the pictures on the walls,
Heroes, fights, and festivals;
And in a corner find the toys
Of the old Egyptian boys.

Robert Louis Stevenson, *A Child's Garden of Verses*

WANDER-THIRST

Beyond the East the sunrise, beyond the West the sea,
And East and West the wander-thirst that will not let me be;
It works in me like madness, dear, to bid me say good-bye;
For the seas call and the stars call, and oh! the call of the sky!

I know not where the white road runs, nor what the blue hills are,
But a man can have the sun for friend, and for his guide a star;
And there's no end of voyaging when once the voice is heard,
For the rivers call and the roads call, and oh! the call of a bird!

Yonder the long horizon lies, and there by night and day
The old ships draw to home again, the young ships sail away;
And come I may, but go I must, and if men ask you why,
You may put the blame on the stars and the sun and the white road
  and the sky.

Gerald Gould, *The Collected Poems of Gerald Gould*
By permission of Mrs. Gerald Gould

TEXAS

When the teacher asks you to bound Texas
Just say it hasn't any bounds.
It's just land, beautiful land, going on and on and on,
Plowed land where each furrow runs straight away to the horizon.

Out of the land boys and girls spring up
And start to grow and keep on growing.
They grow and grow because there's nothing to stop them
Except the sky.
One day they're six feet tall and next day they're seven,
Maybe.
That's the way they grow all over Texas.

The girls are like tall yellow sunflowers with blue eyes,
Or maybe brown.
And the boys are like tall tasseled corn
Swaying graceful and easy in the breeze,
Taking it easy like a steel spring takes it easy
Over the bumps.

There are tall beautiful cities in Texas
Like Fort Worth.
Everything in Fort Worth is big and brand-new.
The most handsome thing in Fort Worth
Are the big handsome white grain elevators
Shining brand-new under a deep blue Texas sky.

In a Texas town they're apt to answer pleasantly and say,
Stranger, we do pretty well around here,
Raise plenty of cotton and lots of cattle,
And just lately we've struck oil.

James Daugherty, *West of Boston*

MAPS

High adventure
  And bright dream—
Maps are mightier
  Than they seem:

Ships that follow
  Leaning stars—
Red and gold of
  Strange bazaars—

Ice floes hid
  Beyond all knowing—
Planes that ride where
  Winds are blowing!

Train maps, maps of
  Wind and weather,
Road maps—taken
  Altogether

Maps are really
  Magic wands
For home-staying
  Vagabonds!

Dorothy Brown Thompson
In *Bridled with Rainbows*
The Macmillan Company, New York, 1949

LET'S PLAY

School is over,
  Oh, what fun!
Lessons finished,
  Play begun.

Girls and boys, come out to play,
The moon doth shine as bright as day;
    Leave your supper, and leave your sleep,
And come with your playfellows into the street.
    Come with a whoop, come with a call,
Come with a good will or not at all.
    Up the ladder and down the wall,
A half-penny roll will serve us all.
    You find milk, and I'll find flour,
And we'll have a pudding in half an hour.

Mother Goose

MY

ZIPPER SUIT

My zipper suit is bunny-brown—
The top zips up, the legs zip down.
I wear it every day.
My daddy brought it out from town.
Zip it up, and zip it down,
And hurry out to play!

Marie Louise Allen
In *Sung under the Silver Umbrella*
The Macmillan Company, New York, 1935

School is over,
    Oh, what fun!
Lessons finished,
    Play begun.
Who'll run fastest,
    You or I?
Who'll laugh loudest?
    Let us try.

Kate Greenaway, *Under the Window*
Frederick Warne and Company, New York and London, 1910

SNIFF

When school is out, we love to follow
our noses over hill and hollow,
smelling jewelweed and vetch,
sniffing fern and milkweed patch.

The airy fifth of our five senses
leads us under, over, fences.
We run like rabbits through bright hours
and poke our noses into flowers!

Frances Frost

In *American Junior Red Cross News*
Copyright 1944 by the American National Red Cross
By permission of the author

As round as an apple, as deep as a cup,
And all the king's horses can't fill it up.

(A Well)

A riddle, a riddle, as I suppose,
A hundred eyes and never a nose!

(A Sieve)

Higher than a house,
Higher than a tree,
Oh! whatever can that be?

(A Star)

Mother Goose

Lives in winter,
Dies in summer,
And grows with its roots upward!

(An Icicle)

A hill full, a hole full,
Yet you cannot catch a bowl full.

(The Mist)

Thirty white horses upon a red hill,
Now they tramp, now they champ,
Now they stand still.

(The Teeth and Gums)

Old Mother Twitchett had but one eye,
And a long tail which she let fly;
And every time she went through a gap,
A bit of her tail she left in a trap.

(A Needle and Thread)

Little Nanny Etticoat
In a white petticoat,
And a red nose;
The longer she stands
The shorter she grows.

(A Candle)

Mother Goose

198

Runs all day and never walks,
Often murmurs, never talks.
It has a bed but never sleeps,
It has a mouth, but never eats.

(A River)

The American Mother Goose (Compiled by Ray Wood)
Copyright 1940 by J. B. Lippincott Company

I have a little sister they call her "Peep-peep,"
She wades in the ocean deep, deep, deep.
She climbs up the mountain high, high, high,
The poor little thing hasn't got but one eye.

(A Star)

The American Mother Goose (Compiled by Ray Wood)
Copyright 1940 by J. B. Lippincott Company

RHYMING RIDDLES

I come more softly than a bird,
And lovely as a flower;
I sometimes last from year to year
And sometimes but an hour.

I stop the swiftest railroad train
Or break the stoutest tree.
And yet I am afraid of fire
And children play with me.

(Snow)

I have no wings, but yet I fly,
I'm slender as a snake and straight as rain,
Who takes me in must die,
Who lets me quickly go will surest gain.

(Arrow)

199

I never speak a word
But when my voice is heard
Even the mountains shake,
No hands I have
And yet great rocks I break.

(Thunder and Lightning)

First I am frosted,
Second, I am beaten,
Third, I am roasted,
Fourth, I am eaten.

(Chestnut)

Mary Austin, from "Seven Rhyming Riddles"
In *The Children Sing in the Far West*
Reprinted by permission of and arrangement with
Houghton Mifflin Company, authorized publishers

To market, to market, to buy a fat pig,
Home again, home again, jiggety jig.

To market, to market, to buy a fat hog,
Home again, home again, jiggety jog.

To market, to market, to buy a plum bun,
Home again, home again, market is done.

Mother Goose

The grand Old Duke of York
   He had ten thousand men,
He marched them up a very high hill
   And he marched them down again.
And when he was up he was up
   And when he was down he was down
And when he was only halfway up
   He was neither up nor down.

Mother Goose

Hippety hop to the barber shop,
To get a stick of candy,
One for you and one for me,
And one for Sister Mandy.

Mother Goose

HOPPITY

Christopher Robin goes
Hoppity, hoppity,
Hoppity, hoppity, hop.
Whenever I tell him
Politely to stop it, he
Says he can't possibly stop.

If he stopped hopping, he couldn't go anywhere,
Poor little Christopher
Couldn't go anywhere . . .
That's why he *always* goes
Hoppity, hoppity,
Hoppity,
Hoppity,
Hop.

A. A. Milne, *When We Were Very Young*

HIPPITY HOP
TO BED

O it's hippity hop to bed!
I'd rather sit up instead.
But when father says "must,"
There's nothing but just
Go hippity hop to bed.

Leroy F. Jackson

Dance to your daddie,
  My bonnie laddie;
Dance to your daddie, my bonnie lamb;
  You shall get a fishy,
  On a little dishy;
You shall get a fishy, when the boat comes home.

Mother Goose

Ride a cock horse
To Banbury Cross
To see a fair lady upon a white horse;
With rings on her fingers,
And bells on her toes,
She shall have music wherever she goes.

Mother Goose

Ride away, ride away,
  Johnny shall ride,
And he shall have pussy-cat
  Tied to one side;
And he shall have little dog
  Tied to the other,
And Johnny shall ride
  To see his grandmother.

Mother Goose

HUSKY HI

(Norwegian)

Husky hi, husky hi,
Here comes Keery galloping by.
She carries her husband tied in a sack,
She carries him home on her horse's back.
Husky hi, husky hi,
Here comes Keery galloping by!

Rose Fyleman, *Picture Rhymes from Foreign Lands*
Copyright 1935 by Rose Fyleman
Reprinted by permission of J. B. Lippincott Company

Master I have, and I am his man,
   Gallop a dreary dun;
Master I have, and I am his man,
   And I'll get a wife as fast as I can;
With a heighly gaily gamberally,
   Higgledy, piggledy, niggledy, niggledy,
   Gallop a dreary dun.

Mother Goose

Jack be nimble,
   Jack be quick,
Jack jump over
   The candlestick.

Jump it lively,
   Jump it quick,
But don't knock over
   The candlestick.

Mother Goose

Here am I, little jumping Joan,
   When nobody's with me
   I'm always alone.

Mother Goose

Jump—jump—jump—
  Jump away
From this town into
  The next, to-day.

Jump—jump—jump—
  Jump over the moon;
Jump all the morning,
  And all the noon.

Jump—jump—jump—
  Jump all night;
Won't our mothers
  Be in a fright?

Jump—jump—jump—
  Over the sea;
What wonderful wonders
  We shall see.

Jump—jump—jump—
  Jump far away;
And all come home
  Some other day.

Kate Greenaway, *Marigold Garden*
Frederick Warne and Company, New York and London, 1910

JUMP

OR

JIGGLE

Frogs jump
Caterpillars hump

Worms wiggle
Bugs jiggle

Rabbits hop
Horses clop

Snakes slide
Sea gulls glide

Mice creep
Deer leap

Puppies bounce
Kittens pounce

Lions stalk—
But—
I walk!

Evelyn Beyer

In *Another Here and Now Story Book,* by Lucy Sprague Mitchell
Published and copyright 1937
by E. P. Dutton & Co., Inc., New York

The pickety fence
The pickety fence
Give it a lick it's
The pickety fence
Give it a lick it's
A clickety fence
Give it a lick it's
A lickety fence
Give it a lick
Give it a lick
Give it a lick
With a rickety stick
Pickety
Pickety
Pickety
Pick

David McCord, *Far and Few*

Copyright 1929, 1931, 1952 by David McCord
By permission of Little, Brown & Company, Boston

Ring-around-a-rosy
A pocket full of posies;
One, two, three,
And we all fall down!

Mother Goose

Little Sally Waters,
Sitting in the sun,
Crying and weeping
For a young man.

Rise, Sally, rise,
Dry your weeping eyes,
Fly to the East, fly to the West,
Fly to the one that you love best.

Mother Goose

Pease porridge hot,
Pease porridge cold,
Pease porridge in the pot,
Nine days old.
Some like it hot,
Some like it cold,
Some like it in the pot,
Nine days old.

Mother Goose

This little pig went to market;
This little pig stayed at home;
This little pig had roast beef;
This little pig had none;
This little pig said, "Wee, wee!
I can't find my way home."

Mother Goose

Higgledy, piggledy, my black hen,
She lays eggs for gentlemen;
Sometimes nine, and sometimes ten,
Higgledy, piggledy, my black hen.

Mother Goose

Intery, mintery, cutery corn,
Apple seed and apple thorn;
Wine, brier, limbυr lock,
Three geese in a flock,
One flew east, one flew west,
And one flew over the goose's nest.

Mother Goose

1, 2, 3, 4, 5!
I caught a hare alive;
6, 7, 8, 9, 10!
I let her go again.

Mother Goose

One, two,
Buckle my shoe;
Three, four,
Knock at the door;
Five, six,
Pick up sticks;
Seven, eight,
Lay them straight;
Nine, ten,
A good, fat hen;

207

Eleven, twelve,
Dig and delve;
Thirteen, fourteen,
Maids a-courting;
Fifteen, sixteen,
Maids in the kitchen;
Seventeen, eighteen,
Maids a-waiting;
Nineteen, twenty,
My plate's empty.

Mother Goose

THE

A B C

BUNNY

A for Apple, big and red
B for Bunny snug a-bed
C for Crash!
D for Dash!
E for Elsewhere in a flash
F for Frog—he's fat and funny
"Looks like rain," says he to Bunny
G for Gale!
H for Hail!
Hippy-hop goes Bunny's tail
I for Insects here and there
J for Jay with jaunty air
K for Kitten, catnip-crazy
L for Lizard—look how lazy
M for Mealtime—munch, munch, munch!
M-m-m these greens are good for lunch
N for Napping in a Nook
O for Owl with bookish look

P for prickly Porcupine
Pins and needles on his spine
Q for Quail
R for Rail
S for Squirrel Swishy-tail
T for Tripping back to Town
U for Up and Up-side-down
V for View
Valley too
W—"We welcome you!"
X for eXit—off, away!
That's enough for us today
Y for You, take one last look
Z for Zero—close the book!

Wanda Gág, *The A B C Bunny*
Copyright 1933 by Wanda Gág
Reprinted by permission of Coward-McCann, Inc.

 A was once an apple-pie,
      Pidy,
      Widy,
      Tidy,
      Pidy,
   Nice insidy,
   Apple-pie!

B was once a little bear,
      Beary,
      Wary,
      Hairy,
      Beary,
   Taky cary,
   Little bear!

209

C was once a little cake,
　　Caky,
　　Baky,
　　Maky,
　　Caky,
　Taky caky,
　Little cake!

D was once a little doll,
　　Dolly,
　　Molly,
　　Polly,
　　Nolly,
　Nursy dolly,
　Little doll!

E was once a little eel,
　　Eely,
　　Weely,
　　Peely,
　　Eely,
　Twirly, tweely,
　Little eel!

F was once a little fish,
　　Fishy,
　　Wishy,
　　Squishy,
　　Fishy,
　In a dishy,
　Little fish!

G was once a little goose,
 Goosy,
 Moosy,
 Boosey,
 Goosey,
 Waddly-woosy,
 Little goose!

H was once a little hen,
 Henny,
 Chenny,
 Tenny,
 Henny,
 Eggsy-any,
 Little hen?

I was once a bottle of ink,
 Inky,
 Dinky,
 Thinky,
 Inky,
 Blacky minky,
 Bottle of ink!

J was once a jar of jam,
 Jammy,
 Mammy,
 Clammy,
 Jammy,
 Sweety, swammy,
 Jar of jam!

K was once a little kite,
    Kity,
    Whity,
    Flighty,
    Kity,
  Out of sighty,
  Little kite!

L was once a little lark,
    Larky,
    Marky,
    Harky,
    Larky,
  In the parky,
  Little lark!

M was once a little mouse,
    Mousy,
    Bousy,
    Sousy,
    Mousy,
  In the housy,
  Little mouse!

N was once a little needle,
    Needly,
    Tweedly,
    Threedly,
    Needly,
  Wisky, wheedly,
  Little needle!

O was once a little owl,
    Owly,
    Prowly,
    Howly,
    Owly,
  Browny fowly,
  Little owl!

P was once a little pump,
    Pumpy,
    Slumpy,
    Flumpy,
    Pumpy,
  Dumpy, thumpy,
  Little pump!

Q was once a little quail,
    Quaily,
    Faily,
    Daily,
    Quaily,
  Stumpy-taily,
  Little quail!

R was once a little rose,
    Rosy,
    Posy,
    Nosy,
    Rosy,
  Blows-y, grows-y,
  Little rose!

S was once a little shrimp,
    Shrimpy,
    Nimpy,
    Flimpy,
    Shrimpy,
Jumpy, jimpy,
Little shrimp!

T was once a little thrush,
    Thrushy,
    Hushy,
    Bushy,
    Thrushy,
Flitty, flushy,
Little thrush!

U was once a little urn,
    Urny,
    Burny,
    Turny,
    Urny,
Bubbly, burny,
Little urn!

V was once a little vine,
    Viny,
    Winy,
    Twiny,
    Viny,
Twisty-twiny,
Little vine!

W was once a whale,
    Whaly,
    Scaly,
    Shaly,
    Whaly,
  Tumbly-taily,
  Mighty whale!

X was once a great king Xerxes,
    Xerxy,
    Perxy,
    Turxy,
    Xerxy,
  Linxy, lurxy,
  Great King Xerxes!

Y was once a little yew,
    Yewdy,
    Fewdy,
    Crudy,
    Yewdy,
  Growdy, grewdy,
  Little yew!

Z was once a piece of zinc,
    Tinky,
    Winky,
    Blinky,
    Tinky,
  Tinky minky,
  Piece of zinc!

Edward Lear

CHOOSING

Which will you have, a ball or a cake?
A cake is so nice, yes, that's what I'll take.

Which will you have, a cake or a cat?
A cat is so soft, I think I'll take that.

Which will you have, a cat or a rose?
A rose is so sweet, I'll have that, I suppose.

Which will you have, a rose or a book?
A book full of pictures?—oh, do let me look!

Which will you have, a book or a ball?
Oh, a ball! No, a book! No, a—
                There! have them all!

SURPRISE

Our uncle called us on the phone
And Plunky answered all alone,
And when he asked what she would like
For a surprise, a motor bike?
Or maybe something nice to wear,
A bit of ribbon for her hair?
Or else a pet, perhaps a pair
Of poodle puppies? or a bear?
Or something she might like to do,
Fly to the moon? or tie her shoe?
Or beat him in a game of chess?
All Plunky answered him was, Yes.

WHAT THE TOYS ARE THINKING

In the jolly, jolly Spring
When we long to leave the shop,
It's the most exciting thing
When any of you stop
And stare and ask the price
Of a Teddy or a top,
Or a baby-doll or Bunny,
Or a little speckled horse.
O, we think it's very nice
When you stand behind the nurses
Counting out what's in your purses;
We are watching you, of course,
Wond'ring what you mean to do,
Hoping, hoping you've the money
And can take us back with you.
But supposing you have not
Quite enough (we cost a lot),
Shake a paw then, stroke a head,
Pat a wistful nose instead,
Whisper in a furry ear,
Comfort us for what we're missing—
Nursery tea and bedtime kissing—
All that never happens here.
You would find it slow yourselves
Sitting still all day on shelves.
Well, next time you're passing through
You'll remember what to do.

In *Merry-Go-Round*, December 1924
By permission of Basil Blackwell & Mott, Ltd., Oxford

THE LOST BALL

Ball's lost, lost, gone,
gone, gone, away.
Rolicky, rollicky
run-away ball!
Ball's rolled away.

Look, look, under, under,
under the table, under the chair.
Spankery, pankery,
naughty, bad ball!
Ball's not there!

Creep, creep, peep, peep,
look in the corner, look on the side.
Hidery, spidery,
hide-away ball!
Please don't hide.

Creep, creep, crawl, crawl
out of the room and into the hall,
round and round.
Peek-a-boo ball!
Come here, my peek-a-boo ball!

Lucy Sprague Mitchell
In *Another Here and Now Story Book*
Published and copyright 1937
by E. P. Dutton & Co., Inc., New York

BLOCK CITY

What are you able to build with your blocks?
Castles and palaces, temples and docks.
Rain may keep raining, and others go roam,
But I can be happy and building at home.

Let the sofa be mountains, the carpet be sea,
There I'll establish a city for me:
A kirk and a mill and a palace beside,
And a harbor as well where my vessels may ride.

Great is the palace with pillar and wall,
A sort of a tower on the top of it all,
And steps coming down in an orderly way
To where my toy vessels lie safe in the bay.

This one is sailing and that one is moored:
Hark to the song of the sailors on board!
And see on the steps of my palace, the kings
Coming and going with presents and things!

Now I have done with it, down let it go!
All in a moment the town is laid low.
Block upon block lying scattered and free,
What is there left of my town by the sea?

Yet as I saw it, I see it again,
The kirk and the palace, the ships and the men,
And as long as I live and where'er I may be,
I'll always remember my town by the sea.

Robert Louis Stevenson, *A Child's Garden of Verses*

Wherever I am, there's always Pooh,
There's always Pooh and Me.
Whatever I do, he wants to do,
"Where are you going to-day?" says Pooh:
"Well, that's very odd 'cos I was too.
Let's go together," says Pooh, says he.
"Let's go together," says Pooh.

"What's twice eleven?" I said to Pooh.
("Twice what?" said Pooh to Me.)
"I *think* it ought to be twenty-two."
"Just what I think myself," said Pooh.
"It wasn't an easy sum to do,
But that's what it is," said Pooh, said he.
"That's what it is," said Pooh.

"Let's look for dragons," I said to Pooh.
"Yes, let's," said Pooh to Me.
We crossed the river and found a few—
"Yes, those are dragons all right," said Pooh.
"As soon as I saw their beaks I knew.
That's what they are," said Pooh, said he.
"That's what they are," said Pooh.

"Let's frighten the dragons," I said to Pooh.
"That's right," said Pooh to Me.
"*I'm* not afraid," I said to Pooh,
And I held his paw and I shouted "Shoo!
Silly old dragons!"—and off they flew.
"I wasn't afraid," said Pooh, said he,
"I'm *never* afraid with you."

So wherever I am, there's always Pooh,
There's always Pooh and Me.
"What would I do?" I said to Pooh,
"If it wasn't for you," and Pooh said: "True,
It isn't much fun for One, but Two
Can stick together," says Pooh, says he.
"That's how it is," says Pooh.

A. A. Milne, *Now We Are Six*

 I once had a sweet little doll, dears,
   The prettiest doll in the world;
Her cheeks were so red and so white, dears,
   And her hair was so charmingly curled.
But I lost my poor little doll, dears,
   As I played in the heath one day;
And I cried for her more than a week, dears,
   But I never could find where she lay.
I found my poor little doll, dears,
   As I played in the heath one day:
Folk say she is terribly changed, dears,
   For her paint is all washed away,
And her arm trodden off by the cows, dears,
   And her hair not the least bit curled:
Yet, for old sakes' sake she is still, dears,
   The prettiest doll in the world.

Charles Kingsley

All the bells were ringing
And all the birds were singing,
When Molly sat down crying
  For her broken doll:
  O you silly Moll!
Sobbing and sighing
  For a broken doll,
When all the bells are ringing,
And all the birds are singing.

Christina Georgina Rossetti, Sing-Song

WINDY MORNING

Who minds if the wind whistles and howls
  When sun makes a wall of pleasant light,
Who minds if beyond the wind owls
  Are hooting as if it still were night!

I know the night is somewhere stalking
  Singing birds, and high in tall
Far away air owls are talking,
  But I don't care if they do at all.

Inside a wall of pleasant sun,
  Inside a wall of the wind's noise
My room is still, and there's much to be done
  With paper and paste and trains and toys.

Harry Behn, Windy Morning

WHAT TO DO

What to do on a rainy day;
What to do
What to do.
There must be a new kind of game to play;
I wish I knew
I wish I knew.

Sister is dressing her dolls again;
They're fine for her
They're fine for her.
Cat and Kitten are washing themselves,
Cleaning their fur
Cleaning their fur.

What to do while it rains outside;
Where to go
Where to go.
I've already eaten, I've already napped;
And the time goes slow
The time goes slow.

But now I see some blue in the sky;
I see some blue
I see some blue.
The clouds are parting, the wind has changed;
And the rain is through
The rain is through!

And soon I'll be out of the house again;
I'll run and shout
I'll run and shout.
I can think of a dozen things to do,
When the sun is out
When the sun is out.

William Wise, *Jonathan Blake*

Published by Alfred A. Knopf, Inc., New York
Copyright © 1956 by William Wise
By permission of the author and the publisher

THE LITTLE RED SLED

"Come out with me!" cried the little red sled.
"I'll give you the wings of a bird," it said.
"The ground is all snowy;
The wind is all blowy!
We'll go like a fairy,
So light and so airy!"

Jocelyn Bush

SKATING

When I try to skate,
My feet are so wary
They grit and they grate:
And then I watch Mary
Easily gliding,
Like an ice-fairy;
Skimming and curving,
Out and in,
With a turn of her head,
And a lift of her chin,
And a gleam of her eye,
And a twirl and a spin;
Sailing under
The breathless hush
Of the willows, and back
To the frozen rush;
Out to the island
And round the edge,
Skirting the rim
Of the crackling sedge,
Swerving close
To the poplar root,
And round the lake
On a single foot,

224

With a three, and an eight,
And a loop and a ring;
Where Mary glides,
The lake will sing!
Out in the mist
I hear her now
Under the frost
Of the willow-bough
Easily sailing,
Light and fleet,
With the song of the lake
Beneath her feet.

Herbert Asquith, *Pillicock Hill*
Reprinted by permission of The Macmillan Company
By permission also of the author and William Heinemann, Ltd.

THE HUNTSMEN

Three jolly gentlemen,
  In coats of red,
Rode their horses
  Up to bed.

Three jolly gentlemen
  Snored till morn,
Their horses champing
  The golden corn.

Three jolly gentlemen,
  At break of day,
Came clitter-clatter down the stairs
  And galloped away.

Walter de la Mare, *Collected Poems, 1901–1918*
Copyright 1920 by Henry Holt and Company, Inc.
Copyright 1948 by Walter de la Mare
Reprinted by permission of the publishers
(Also in *Rhymes and Verses* by Walter de la Mare
Published by Henry Holt and Company, Inc., New York, 1947)

WINGS

AND

WHEELS

Ahoy and ahoy, birds!
We cannot have wings
And feathers and things,
But dashing on wheels
With the wind at our heels
Is almost like flying—
Such joy, birds!

Oho and oho, birds!
Of course we can't rise
Up and up to the skies;
But skimming and sliding
On rollers, and gliding,
Is almost as jolly,
You know, birds!

Nancy Byrd Turner, *Magpie Lane*
Copyright 1927 by Harcourt, Brace and Company, Inc., New York
Copyright 1956 by Nancy Byrd Turner

DIFFERENT

BICYCLES

When I ride my bicycle
I pedal and pedal
Knees up, knees down.
Knees up, knees down.

But when the boy next door
Rides his,
It's whizz—
A chuck   a chuck—

And away
He's gone
With his
Knees steady-straight

In one place . . .
Because—
   His bicycle has
   A motor fastened on.

Dorothy Baruch, *I Like Machinery*

THE

SWING

How do you like to go up in a swing,
   Up in the air so blue?
Oh, I do think it the pleasantest thing
   Ever a child can do!

Up in the air and over the wall,
   Till I can see so wide,
Rivers and trees and cattle and all
   Over the countryside—

Till I look down on the garden green,
   Down on the roof so brown—
Up in the air I go flying again,
   Up in the air and down!

Robert Louis Stevenson, *A Child's Garden of Verses*

SLIDING

Down the slide
We ride, we ride.
Round we run, and then
   Up we pop
   To reach the top,
Down we come again.

Marchette Chute
Copyright 1946 by Marchette Chute
From *Around and About* by Marchette Chute
Published by E. P. Dutton & Co., Inc., New York, 1957

227

THE
FISHERMAN

The little boy is fishing
With a green fishline,
And he has got me wishing
That his line were mine.

The little boy is fishing
With a fresh-cut pole,
And he has got me wishing
For his fishing hole.

The little boy is fishing
With better than a pin,
And he has got me wishing
That he won't fall in.

The little boy is fishing
With a disenchanted slug,
And he has got me wishing
For the first faint tug.

The little boy is fishing
With a cider-cork float,
And he has got me wishing
For the cider and a boat.

The little boy is fishing
For I don't know what,
And he has got my wishing
In an awful knot.

David McCord, *Far and Few*
Copyright 1929, 1931, 1952 by David McCord
By permission of Little, Brown & Company, Boston

PICNIC DAY

Sing a song of picnics,
 Bread and butter spread,
Greenery all around about,
 And cherries overhead!

Rachel Field, *A Little Book of Days*
Copyright 1927 by Doubleday & Company, Inc.

AT THE SEA-SIDE

When I was down beside the sea
A wooden spade they gave to me
 To dig the sandy shore.

My holes were empty like a cup.
In every hole the sea came up,
 Till it could come no more.

Robert Louis Stevenson, *A Child's Garden of Verses*

SKIPPING ALONG ALONE

Oh, how I love to skip alone
 Along the beach in moisty weather;
The whole world seems my very own,
Each fluted shell and glistening stone,
 Each wave that twirls a silver feather.

I skip along so brave and big
 Behind the sand-birds gray and tiny,
I love to see their quick feet jig,
Each leaves a mark, neat as a twig,
 Stamped in the sand so clear and shiny.

And fine and faint as drops of spray
 I hear their little voices calling,
"Sweet, sweet! Sweet, sweet!" I hear them say—
I love to skip alone and play
 Along the sand when mist is falling.

Winifred Welles, *Skipping Along Alone*
The Macmillan Company, New York, 1931

229

SAND-BETWEEN-THE-TOES

I went down to the shouting sea,
Taking Christopher down with me,
For Nurse had given us sixpence each—
And down we went to the beach.

> We had sand in the eyes and the ears and the nose,
> And sand in the hair, and sand-between-the-toes.
> Whenever a good nor'wester blows,
> Christopher is certain of
> Sand-between-the-toes.

The sea was galloping grey and white;
Christopher clutched his sixpence tight;
We clambered over the humping sand—
And Christopher held my hand.

> We had sand in the eyes and the ears and the nose,
> And sand in the hair, and sand-between-the-toes.
> Whenever a good nor'wester blows,
> Christopher is certain of
> Sand-between-the-toes.

There was a roaring in the sky;
The sea-gulls cried as they blew by;
We tried to talk, but had to shout—
Nobody else was out.

> When we got home, we had sand in the hair,
> In the eyes and the ears and everywhere;
> Whenever a good nor'wester blows,
> Christopher is found with
> Sand-between-the-toes.

A. A. Milne, *When We Were Very Young*

Copyright 1924 by E. P. Dutton & Co., Inc.
Renewal 1952 by A. A. Milne
By permission of E. P. Dutton & Co., Inc., New York
and Methuen & Co., Ltd., London

BEACH FIRE

When the picnic was over,
We sat by the tide
And watched the white-winged
Sea gulls slide

Down the evening wind.
The stars came out
Above the sea,
And Dad gave a shout:

"Oh, wish on that little
Brand-new moon!
Let's build up the fire
With wood from the dune!"

We wished on the moon,
We built up the fire,
We sang, while the sparks
Flew higher, higher,

Like stars of our own
Above the foam,
Till, sleepy, we
And the birds went home.

Frances Frost, *The Little Whistler*
Whittlesey House, McGraw-Hill Book Company, Inc., New York, 1949

WHERE GO THE BOATS?

Dark brown is the river,
  Golden is the sand.
It flows along forever,
  With trees on either hand.

Green leaves a-floating,
  Castles of the foam,
Boats of mine a-boating—
  Where will all come home?

On goes the river
  And out past the mill,
Away down the valley,
  Away down the hill.

Away down the river,
  A hundred miles or more,
Other little children
  Shall bring my boats ashore.

Robert Louis Stevenson, *A Child's Garden of Verses*

THE LITTLE WHISTLER

My mother whistled softly,
My father whistled bravely,
My brother whistled merrily,
And I tried all day long!
I blew my breath inwards,
I blew my breath outwards,
But all you heard was breath blowing
And not a bit of song!

But today I heard a bluebird,
A happy, young, and new bird,
Whistling in the apple tree—
He'd just discovered how!
Then quick I blew my breath in,
And gay I blew my breath out,
And sudden I blew three wild notes—
And I can whistle now!

Frances Frost, *The Little Whistler*
Whittlesey House, McGraw-Hill Book Company, Inc., New York, 1949

HAPPINESS

John had
Great Big
Waterproof
Boots on;
John had a
Great Big
Waterproof
Hat;
John had a
Great Big
Waterproof
Mackintosh—
And that
(Said John)
Is
That.

A. A. Milne, *When We Were Very Young*

Copyright 1924 by E. P. Dutton & Co., Inc., New York
Renewal 1952 by A. A. Milne
By permission of the publishers

It's fun to go out and buy new shoes to wear,
To go to the shoe store and pick out a pair
Of slippers with zippers or boots big and square—
It's fun to go shopping for shoes.

Mary Ann Hoberman, *All My Shoes Come in Twos*

CHOOSING
SHOES

New shoes, new shoes,
    Red and pink and blue shoes.
Tell me, what would *you* choose,
    If they'd let us buy?

Buckle shoes, bow shoes,
    Pretty pointy-toe shoes,
Strappy, cappy low shoes;
    Let's have some to try.

Bright shoes, white shoes,
    Dandy-dance-by-night shoes,
Perhaps-a-little-tight shoes,
    Like some? So would I.

But

Flat shoes, fat shoes,
    Stump-along-like-that shoes,
Wipe-them-on-the-mat shoes,
    That's the sort they'll buy.

Ffrida Wolfe, *The Very Thing*
Sidgwick and Jackson, Ltd., London, 1928

234

NEW SHOES

I have new shoes in the Fall-time
And new ones in the Spring.
Whenever I wear my new shoes
I always have to sing!

Alice Wilkins
In *The Golden Flute*
The John Day Company, Inc., New York, 1932

MARCHING SONG

Bring the comb and play upon it!
   Marching, here we come!
Willie cocks his highland bonnet,
   Johnnie beats the drum.

Mary Jane commands the party,
   Peter leads the rear;
Feet in time, alert and hearty,
   Each a Grenadier!

All in the most martial manner
   Marching double-quick;
While the napkin, like a banner,
   Waves upon the stick!

Here's enough of fame and pillage,
   Great commander Jane!
Now that we've been round the village,
   Let's go home again.

Robert Louis Stevenson, *A Child's Garden of Verses*

AWAY WE GO

Mother plays a march
and so
away we go, away we go . . .
past a forest made of chairs,
up the mountain of the stairs,
past a den of bears . . .
and so
away we go, away we go.

Music makes us march,
you know,
away we go, away we go . . .
Nancy with a paper cap
and Edward with a haversack
and Bunny at the back,
and so
away we go, away we go.

Houses may be small,
but oh,
away we go, away we go . . .
through the cavern of the door,
over meadows of the floor,
over hills galore . . .
and so
away we go, away we go.

Aileen Fisher, *Up the Windy Hill*

HALFWAY
DOWN

Halfway down the stairs
Is a stair
Where I sit.
There isn't any
Other stair
Quite like
It.
I'm not at the bottom,
I'm not at the top;
So this is the stair
Where
I always
Stop.

Halfway up the stairs
Isn't up,
And isn't down.
It isn't in the nursery,
It isn't in the town.
And all sorts of funny thoughts
Run round my head:
"It isn't really
Anywhere!
It's somewhere else
Instead!"

A. A. Milne, *When We Were Very Young*

Every time I climb a tree
Every time I climb a tree
Every time I climb a tree
I scrape a leg
Or skin a knee
And every time I climb a tree
I find some ants
Or dodge a bee
And get the ants
All over me

And every time I climb a tree
Where have you been?
They say to me
But don't they know that I am free
Every time I climb a tree?
I like it best
To spot a nest
That has an egg
Or maybe three

And then I skin
The other leg
But every time I climb a tree
I see a lot of things to see
Swallows rooftops and TV
And all the fields and farms there be
Every time I climb a tree
Though climbing may be good for ants
It isn't awfully good for pants
But still it's pretty good for me
Every time I climb a tree

David McCord, *Far and Few*

MY SHADOW

I have a little shadow that goes in and out with me,
And what can be the use of him is more than I can see.
He is very, very like me from the heels up to the head;
And I see him jump before me, when I jump into my bed.

The funniest thing about him is the way he likes to grow—
Not at all like proper children, which is always very slow;
For he sometimes shoots up taller like an India-rubber ball,
And he sometimes gets so little that there's none of him at all.

He hasn't got a notion of how children ought to play,
And can only make a fool of me in every sort of way.
He stays so close beside me, he's a coward you can see;
I'd think shame to stick to nursie as that shadow sticks to me!

One morning, very early, before the sun was up,
I rose and found the shining dew on every buttercup;
But my lazy little shadow, like an arrant sleepy-head,
Had stayed at home behind me and was fast asleep in bed.

Robert Louis Stevenson, A Child's Garden of Verses

SHADOW DANCE

O Shadow,
Dear Shadow,
Come, Shadow,
And dance!
On the wall
In the firelight
Let both of
Us prance!
I raise my
Arms, thus!
And you raise
Your arms, so!
And dancing
And leaping
And laughing
We go!
From the wall
To the ceiling,
From ceiling
To wall,
Just you and
I, Shadow,
And none else
At all.

Ivy O. Eastwick, *Fairies and Suchlike*
Published and copyright 1946 by E. P. Dutton & Co., Inc., New York

MUSIC

Can you dance?
I love to dance!
Music is my happy chance.
Music playing
In the street
Gets into
My hands and feet.

Can you sing?
I love to sing!
Music, like a bird in Spring,
With a gold
And silver note
Gets into
My heart and throat.

Can you play?
I'd love to play!
Practise music every day—
Then you'll give
The world a chance
To dance and sing,
To sing and dance.

Eleanor Farjeon, *Poems for Children*

Copyright 1951 by Eleanor Farjeon
Published by J. B. Lippincott Co., Philadelphia

HIDING

I'm hiding, I'm hiding,
And no one knows where;
For all they can see is my
Toes and my hair.

And I just heard my father
Say to my mother—
"But, darling, he must be
Somewhere or other;

"Have you looked in the ink well?"
And Mother said, "Where?"
"In the INK WELL," said Father. But
I was not there.

Then "Wait!" cried my mother—
"I think that I see
Him under the carpet." But
It was not me.

"Inside the mirror's
A pretty good place,"
Said Father and looked, but saw
Only his face.

"We've hunted," sighed Mother,
"As hard as we could
And I AM so afraid that we've
Lost him for good."

Then I laughed out aloud
And I wiggled my toes
And Father said—"Look, dear,
I wonder if those

Toes could be Benny's.
There are ten of them. See?"
And they WERE so surprised to find
Out it was me!

Dorothy Aldis, *Everything and Anything*
Minton, Balch and Company, New York, 1927
Copyright 1925, 1926, 1927 by Dorothy Aldis

FUN IN A GARRET

We're having a lovely time to-day!
We're all of us up in the garret at play!
We have three houses under the eaves—
Not real, you know, but make-believes;
Two we live in, and one is a store,
Where a little old screen makes a truly door.
Warren keeps store, and Joe is his clerk,
And Betty and I stay at home and work.
Joe comes around and knocks or rings,
And we order potatoes and steaks and things;
And sometimes we go to the store and buy,
Or send the children for ribbons or pie.
It's lots of fun—just try it some day
When it rains too hard to go out and play.

Emma C. Dowd, *The Owl and the Bobolink*
Houghton Mifflin Company, Boston, 1914

A GOOD PLAY

We built a ship upon the stairs
All made of the back-bedroom **chairs,**
And filled it full of sofa pillows
To go a-sailing on the billows.

We took a saw and several nails,
And water in the nursery pails;
And Tom said, "Let us also take
An apple and a slice of cake;"—
Which was enough for Tom and me
To go a-sailing on, till tea.

We sailed along for days and days,
And had the very best of plays;
But Tom fell out and hurt his knee,
So there was no one left but me.

Robert Louis Stevenson, *A Child's Garden of Verses*

PIRATE STORY

Three of us afloat in the meadow by the swing,
   Three of us aboard in the basket on the lea.
Winds are in the air, they are blowing in the spring,
   And waves are on the meadow like the waves there are at sea.

Where shall we adventure, to-day that we're afloat,
   Wary of the weather and steering by a star?
Shall it be to Africa, a-steering of the boat,
   To Providence, or Babylon, or off to Malabar?

Hi! but here's a squadron a-rowing on the sea—
   Cattle on the meadow a-charging with a roar!
Quick, and we'll escape them, they're as mad as they can be,
   The wicket is the harbour and the garden is the shore.

Robert Louis Stevenson, *A Child's Garden of Verses*

THE LAND OF STORY-BOOKS

At evening when the lamp is lit,
Around the fire my parents sit;
They sit at home and talk and sing,
And do not play at anything.

Now, with my little gun, I crawl
All in the dark along the wall,
And follow round the forest track
Away behind the sofa back.

There, in the night, where none can spy,
All in my hunter's camp I lie,
And play at books that I have read
Till it is time to go to bed.

These are the hills, these are the woods,
These are my starry solitudes;
And there the river by whose brink
The roaring lions come to drink.

I see the others far away
As if in firelit camp they lay,
And I, like to an Indian scout,
Around their party prowled about.

So, when my nurse comes in for me,
Home I return across the sea,
And go to bed with backward looks
At my dear Land of Story-books.

Robert Louis Stevenson, *A Child's Garden of Verses*

BEDTIME

Five minutes, five minutes more, please!
  Let me stay five minutes more!
Can't I just finish the castle
  I'm building here on the floor?
Can't I just finish the story
  I'm reading here in my book?
Can't I just finish this bead-chain—
  It *almost* is finished, look!
Can't I just finish this game, please?
  When a game's once begun
It's a pity never to find out
  Whether you've lost or won.
Can't I just stay five minutes?
  Well, can't I stay just four?
Three minutes, then? two minutes?
  Can't I stay *one* minute more?

Eleanor Farjeon, *Over the Garden Wall*
Copyright 1933 by Eleanor Farjeon
Reprinted by permission of J. B. Lippincott Company
(Also in *Poems for Children* by Eleanor Farjeon
Published by J. B. Lippincott Company, Philadelphia and New York
Copyright 1951 by Eleanor Farjeon)

LITTLE MISS PITT

"Is it really very far
To Zanzibar?"
Jonathan said to Miss Pitt.

"And have you been to Spain,
Or gone fishing up in Maine
With a guide who plays a beautiful guitar?

"If you lived in Cuba
Would you buy yourself a tuba?"
Jonathan said to Miss Pitt.

"Or if you lived in Dallas,
Would it be inside a palace—?"
But Jonathan had gone a bit too far.

Little Miss Pitt
Was noted for her wit;
She was famous for her speed of repartee:

"O Jonathan Blake,
You have made a mistake
When you tried to act clever with me.

"Of course it's quite far
To Zanzibar;
And Maine and sunny Spain I've both seen.
And if I lived in Cuba
I would own a silver tuba;
While in Dallas I'd have a palace for a queen.

"Now your questions I've answered,
I've answered them all—
So it's *my* turn to ask one instead.
Which boy thinks it's clever
To ask questions forever,
When it's time he was upstairs in bed?"

William Wise, *Jonathan Blake*

Published by Alfred A. Knopf, Inc., New York
Copyright © 1956 by William Wise
By permission of author and publisher

MRS. BROWN

As soon as I'm in bed at night
And snugly settled down,
The little girl I am by day
Goes very suddenly away,
And then I'm Mrs. Brown.

I have a family of six,
And all of them have names,
The girls are Joyce and Nancy Maud,
The boys are Marmaduke and Claude
And Percival and James.

We have a house with twenty rooms
A mile away from town;
I think it's good for girls and boys
To be allowed to make a noise—
And so does Mr. Brown.

We do the most exciting things,
Enough to make you creep;
And on and on and on we go—
I sometimes wonder if I know
When I have gone to sleep.

Rose Fyleman, *The Fairy Green*

THINGS

Trains are for going,
Boats are for rowing,
Seeds are for sowing,
Noses for blowing,
    And sleeping's for bed.

Dogs are for pawing,
Logs are for sawing,
Crows are for cawing,
Rivers for thawing,
    And sleeping's for bed.

Flags are for flying,
Stores are for buying,
Glasses for spying,
Babies for crying,
    And sleeping's for bed.

Cows are for mooing,
Chickens for shooing,
Blue is for bluing,
Things are for doing,
    And sleeping's for bed.

Games are for playing,
Hay is for haying,
Horses for neighing,
Saying's for saying,
    And sleeping's for bed.

Money's for spending,
Patients for tending,
Branches for bending,
Poems for ending,
    And sleeping's for bed.

William Jay Smith, *Laughing Time*
Copyright 1955 by William Jay Smith
By permission of Little, Brown & Company, Boston

OVER

AND

UNDER

Bridges are for going over water,
Boats are for going over sea;
Dots are for going over dotted *i*'s,
And blankets are for going over me.

Over and under,
Over and under,
Crack the whip,
And hear the thunder.

Divers are for going under water,
Seals are for going under sea;
Fish are for going under mermaids' eyes,
And pillows are for going under me.

Over and under,
Over and under,
Crack the whip,
And hear the thunder,
Crack-crack-crack,
Hear the crack of thunder!

William Jay Smith, *Laughing Time*

MERRY-

GO-

ROUND

I climbed up on the merry-go-round,
And it went round and round.
I climbed up on a big brown horse
And it went up and down.
Around and round
And up and down,
Around and round
And up and down,

I sat high up
On a big brown horse
And rode around
On the merry-go-round
   And rode around
On the merry-go-round
I rode around
On the merry-go-round
   Around
      And round
   And
      Round.

Dorothy Baruch, *I Like Machinery*
Harper & Brothers, New York, 1933

DRINKING

FOUNTAIN

When I climb up
   To get a drink,
It doesn't work
   The way you'd think.

I turn it up.
   The water goes
And hits me right
   Upon the nose.

I turn it down
   To make it small
And don't get any
   Drink at all.

Marchette Chute

Copyright 1946 by Marchette Chute
From *Around and About* by Marchette Chute
Published by E. P. Dutton & Co., Inc., New York, 1957

JUNE

The merry-go-round
    Plays a bouncy tune!
There are flowers on the ground
    And it's June! It's June!
Vacation's here
    And school is done!
We play new games,
    We shout and run!
But best of all to do, we've found
Is to ride and sing on the merry-go-round.

There's a tall giraffe,
    There's an ostrich white.
We all climb on,
    We hold them tight.
The music begins, and we like the sound!
And we fly through the air on the merry-go-round!

Mary Carolyn Davies
In *Child Life,* June 1938
Copyright 1938 by Rand McNally & Co., Chicago

THE CIRCUS PARADE

O Goody, it's coming, the circus parade
    And all the way up the street,
What crowds of people in gay-colored clothes,
    With popcorn and peanuts to eat!

The children have red, blue, and yellow balloons,
    As up by the curbing they stand,
And now, in the distance, we suddenly hear
    The circus's big brass band!

Behind the crash-bang! of the music they play,
    Come riders in red velvet gowns,
And after them doing the funniest things,
    A silly procession of clowns.

Then lions and tigers that pace up and down,
    In wagons all painted with gold,
And monkeys a-playing just all kinds of tricks,
    As they grimace and chatter and scold.

O, next there come camels and elephants, too,
    High on their backs men ride;
There are queer little ponies, no bigger than dogs,
    With a clown on a donkey, beside!

And then there come chariots rumbling by
    With horses all four in a row;
And the wheezing, old, piping calliope is
    The very tail end of the show!

Olive Beaupré Miller
In *My Book House*

Used by permission of the author and the publishers,
The Book House for Children, Lake Bluff, Illinois

C is for the Circus
   Which springtime brings to town.
(The country has its crocus,
   But we much prefer the clown.)
C's for canes and cracker-jack
   And curious camels, too.
I wouldn't trade a Circus
   For some crocuses. Would you?

Phyllis McGinley, *All Around the Town*

I meant to do my work to-day—
   But a brown bird sang in the apple-tree,
And a butterfly flitted across the field,
   And all the leaves were calling me.

And the wind went sighing over the land,
   Tossing the grasses to and fro,
And a rainbow held out its shining hand—
   So what could I do but laugh and go?

Richard LeGallienne, *The Lonely Dancer*

JILL CAME FROM THE FAIR

Jill came from the Fair
With her pennies all spent.
She had had her full share
Of delight and content;
She had ridden the ring
To a wonderful tune,
She had flown in a swing
Half as high as the moon,
In a boat that was drawn
By an ivory swan
Beside a green lawn
On a lake she had gone,
She had bought a gold packet
That held her desire,
She had touched the red jacket
Of one who ate fire,
She had stood at the butt,
And although she was small
She had won a rough nut
With the throw of a ball,
And across the broad back
Of a donkey a-straddle,
She had jolted like Jack-
In-the-Box on a saddle—
Till mid frolic and shout
And tinsel and litter,
The lights started out
Making everything glitter,
And dazed by the noise
And the blare and the flare,
With her toys and her joys
Jill came from the Fair.

Eleanor Farjeon, *Over the Garden Wall*
Copyright 1933 by Eleanor Farjeon
Reprinted by permission of J. B. Lippincott Company
(Also in *Poems for Children* by Eleanor Farjeon
Published by J. B. Lippincott Company, Philadelphia and New York
Copyright 1951 by Eleanor Farjeon)

LAUGHING

SONG

When the green woods laugh with the voice of joy,
And the dimpling stream runs laughing by;
When the air does laugh with our merry wit,
And the green hill laughs with the noise of it;

When the meadows laugh with lively green,
And the grasshopper laughs in the merry scene;
When Mary and Susan and Emily
With their sweet round mouths sing, "Ha ha he!"

When the painted birds laugh in the shade,
When our table with cherries and nuts is spread;
Come live, and be merry, and join with me,
To sing the sweet chorus of "Ha ha he!"

William Blake

MERRY

ARE

THE

BELLS

Merry are the bells, and merry would they ring,
Merry was myself, and merry could I sing;
With a merry ding-dong, happy, gay, and free,
And a merry sing-song, happy let us be!

Merry have we met, and merry have we been;
Merry let us part, and merry meet again;
With our merry sing-song, happy, gay, and free,
With a merry ding-dong, happy let us be!

Unknown

HOW
RIDICULOUS

Hey, diddle, diddle!
The cat and the fiddle,
The cow jumped over the moon.

Hey, diddle, diddle!
The cat and the fiddle,
The cow jumped over the moon;
The little dog laughed
To see such sport,
And the dish ran away with the spoon.

Mother Goose

THE LITTLE KITTENS

"Where are you going, my little kittens?"
"We are going to town to get us some mittens."
   "What! Mittens for kittens!
   Do kittens wear mittens?
Who ever saw little kittens with mittens?"

"Where are you going, my little cat?"
"I am going to town to get me a hat."
   "What! A hat for a cat!
   A cat get a hat!
Who ever saw a cat with a hat?"

"Where are you going, my little pig?"
"I am going to town to get me a wig."
   "What! A wig for a pig!
   A pig in a wig!
Who ever saw a pig in a wig?"

Eliza Lee Follen

THE CATS' TEA-PARTY

Five little pussy-cats, invited out to tea,
Cried: "Mother, let us go—Oh do! for good we'll surely be.
We'll wear our bibs and hold our things as you have shown us how—
Spoons in right paws, cups in left—and make a pretty bow;
We'll always say 'Yes, if you please,' and 'Only half of that.'"
"Then go, my darling children," said the happy Mother Cat.
The five little pussy-cats went out that night to tea.
Their heads were smooth and glossy, their tails were swinging free;
They held their things as they had learned, and tried to be
    polite;—
With snowy bibs beneath their chins they were a pretty sight.
But, alas, for manners beautiful, and coats as soft as silk!
The moment that the little kits were asked to take some milk,
They dropped their spoons, forgot to bow, and—oh, what do you
    think?
They put their noses in the cups and all began to drink!
Yes, every naughty little kit set up a mew for more,
Then knocked their tea-cups over, and scampered through the door.

Frederick E. Weatherly

THE DUEL

The gingham dog and the calico cat
Side by side on the table sat;
'T was half-past twelve, and (what do you
        think!)
Nor one nor t' other had slept a wink!
    The old Dutch clock and the Chinese plate
    Appeared to know as sure as fate
There was going to be a terrible spat.
    (*I wasn't there; I simply state*
    What was told to me by the Chinese plate!)

259

The gingham dog went, "bow-wow-wow!"
And the calico cat replied, "mee-ow!"
The air was littered, an hour or so,
With bits of gingham and calico,
    While the old Dutch clock in the chimney-
        place
Up with its hands before its face,
For it always dreaded a family row!
    (Now mind: I'm only telling you
    What the old Dutch clock declares is true!)

The Chinese plate looked very blue,
And wailed, "Oh, dear! what shall we do!"
But the gingham dog and the calico cat
Wallowed this way and tumbled that,
    Employing every tooth and claw
    In the awfullest way you ever saw—
And, oh! how the gingham and calico flew!
    (Don't fancy I exaggerate—
    I got my news from the Chinese plate!)

Next morning, where the two had sat
They found no trace of dog or cat;
And some folks think unto this day
That burglars stole that pair away!
    But the truth about the cat and pup
    Is this: they ate each other up!
Now what do you really think of that!
    (The old Dutch clock it told me so,
    And that is how I came to know.)

Eugene Field, *Poems of Childhood*
Charles Scribner's Sons, New York, 1904

THE OWL AND THE PUSSY-CAT

The Owl and the Pussy-Cat went to sea
   In a beautiful pea-green boat,
They took some honey, and plenty of money
   Wrapped up in a five-pound note.
The Owl looked up to the stars above,
   And sang to a small guitar,
"O lovely Pussy, O Pussy, my love,
   What a beautiful Pussy you are,
         You are,
         You are!
   What a beautiful Pussy you are!"

Pussy said to the Owl, "You elegant fowl,
   How charmingly sweet you sing!
Oh! let us be married, too long we have tarried:
   But what shall we do for a ring?"
They sailed away, for a year and a day,
   To the land where the Bong-tree grows;
And there in a wood a Piggy-wig stood,
   With a ring at the end of his nose,
         His nose,
         His nose,
   With a ring at the end of his nose.

"Dear Pig, are you willing to sell for one shilling
   Your ring?" Said the Piggy, "I will."
So they took it away, and were married next day
   By the Turkey who lives on the hill.
They dined on mince and slices of quince,
   Which they ate with a runcible spoon;
And hand in hand, on the edge of the sand,
   They danced by the light of the moon,
         The moon,
         The moon,
   They danced by the light of the moon.

Edward Lear

THE RUM
TUM
TUGGER

The Rum Tum Tugger is a Curious Cat:
If you offer him pheasant he would rather have grouse.
If you put him in a house he would much prefer a flat,
If you put him in a flat then he'd rather have a house.
If you set him on a mouse then he only wants a rat,
If you set him on a rat then he'd rather chase a mouse.
Yes the Rum Tum Tugger is a Curious Cat—
  And there isn't any call for me to shout it:
    For he will do
    As he do do
      And there's no doing anything about it!

The Rum Tum Tugger is a terrible bore:
When you let him in, then he wants to be out;
He's always on the wrong side of every door,
As soon as he's at home, then he'd like to get about.
He likes to lie in the bureau drawer,
But he makes such a fuss if he can't get out.
Yes the Rum Tum Tugger is a Curious Cat—
  And it isn't any use for you to doubt it:
    For he will do
    As he do do
      And there's no doing anything about it!

The Rum Tum Tugger is a curious beast:
His disobliging ways are a matter of habit.
If you offer him fish then he always wants a feast;
When there isn't any fish then he won't eat rabbit.
If you offer him cream then he sniffs and sneers,
For he only likes what he finds for himself;
So you'll catch him in it right up to the ears,
If you put it away on the larder shelf.
The Rum Tum Tugger is artful and knowing,
The Rum Tum Tugger doesn't care for a cuddle;
But he'll leap on your lap in the middle of your sewing,
For there's nothing he enjoys like a horrible muddle.
Yes the Rum Tum Tugger is a Curious Cat—
   And there isn't any need for me to spout it:
      For he will do
      As he do do
         And there's no doing anything about it!

T. S. Eliot, *Old Possum's Book of Practical Cats*

Harcourt, Brace and Company, New York, Copyright 1939
Reprinted by permission of Harcourt, Brace and Company
and Faber and Faber, Limited

MACAVITY:
THE
MYSTERY
CAT

Macavity's a Mystery Cat: he's called the Hidden Paw—
For he's the master criminal who can defy the Law.
He's the bafflement of Scotland Yard, the Flying Squad's despair:
For when they reach the scene of crime—*Macavity's not there!*

Macavity, Macavity, there's no one like Macavity,
He's broken every human law, he breaks the law of gravity.
His powers of levitation would make a fakir stare,
And when you reach the scene of crime—*Macavity's not there!*
You may seek him in the basement, you may look up in the air—
But I tell you once and once again, *Macavity's not there!*

Macavity's a ginger cat, he's very tall and thin;
You would know him if you saw him, for his eyes are sunken in.
His brow is deeply lined with thought, his head is highly domed;
His coat is dusty from neglect, his whiskers are uncombed.
He sways his head from side to side, with movements like a snake;
And when you think he's half asleep, he's always wide awake.

Macavity, Macavity, there's no one like Macavity,
For he's a fiend in feline shape, a monster of depravity.
You may meet him in a by-street, you may see him in the square—
But when a crime's discovered, then *Macavity's not there!*

He's outwardly respectable. (They say he cheats at cards.)
And his footprints are not found in any file of Scotland Yard's.
And when the larder's looted, or the jewel-case is rifled,
Or when the milk is missing, or another Peke's been stifled,
Or the greenhouse glass is broken, and the trellis past repair—
Ay, there's the wonder of the thing! *Macavity's not there!*

And when the Foreign Office find a Treaty's gone astray,
Or the Admiralty lose some plans and drawings by the way,
There may be a scrap of paper in the hall or on the stair—
But it's useless to investigate—*Macavity's not there!*
And when the loss has been disclosed, the Secret Service say:
"It *must* have been Macavity!"—but he's a mile away.
You'll be sure to find him resting, or a-licking of his thumbs,
Or engaged in doing complicated long division sums.

Macavity, Macavity, there's no one like Macavity,
There never was a Cat of such deceitfulness and suavity.
He always has an alibi, and one or two to spare:
At whatever time the deed took place—MACAVITY WASN'T
    THERE!
And they say that all the Cats whose wicked deeds are widely
    known,
(I might mention Mungojerrie, I might mention Griddlebone)
Are nothing more than agents for the Cat who all the time
Just controls their operations: the Napoleon of Crime!

T. S. Eliot, *Old Possum's Book of Practical Cats*

Harcourt, Brace and Company, New York, Copyright 1939
Reprinted by permission of Harcourt, Brace and Company
and Faber and Faber, Limited

Sing a song of sixpence,
  A pocket full of rye;
Four-and-twenty blackbirds
  Baked in a pie!

When the pie was opened
  The birds began to sing;
Was not that a dainty dish
  To set before the king?

The king was in his counting-house
  Counting out his money;
The queen was in the parlor,
  Eating bread and honey.

The maid was in the garden,
  Hanging out the clothes;
When down came a blackbird
  And snapped off her nose.

Mother Goose

A farmer went trotting upon his gray mare;
  Bumpety, bumpety, bump!
With his daughter behind him so rosy and fair;
  Lumpety, lumpety, lump!

A raven cried "Croak!" and they all tumbled down,
  Bumpety, bumpety, bump!
The mare broke her knees, and the farmer his crown,
  Lumpety, lumpety, lump!

The mischievous raven flew laughing away,
  Bumpety, bumpety, bump!
And vowed he would serve them the same the next day,
  Lumpety, lumpety, lump!

Mother Goose

Hickory, dickory, dock!
The mouse ran up the clock;
  The clock struck One,
  The mouse ran down,
Hickory, dickory, dock!

Mother Goose

I saw a ship a-sailing,
A-sailing on the sea;
And, oh! it was all laden
With pretty things for thee!

There were comfits in the cabin,
And apples in the hold;
The sails were made of silk,
And the masts were made of gold.

The four-and-twenty sailors
That stood between the decks,
Were four-and-twenty white mice
With chains about their necks.

The captain was a duck,
With a packet on his back;
And when the ship began to move,
The captain said, "Quack! Quack!"

Mother Goose

When a goose meets a moose
At the house of a mouse
I wonder if all three
Sit down and drink tea.

Zhenya Gay, Jingle Jangle

Higgledy, piggledy! see how they run!
Hopperty, popperty! what is the fun?
Has the sun or the moon tumbled into the sea?
What is the matter, now? Pray tell it me!

Higgledy, piggledy! how can I tell?
Hopperty, popperty! hark to the bell!
The rats and the mice even scamper away;
Who can say what may not happen to-day?

Kate Greenaway, *Under the Window*
Frederick Warne and Company, New York and London, 1910

THE DOG'S
COLD NOSE

When Noah, perceiving 'twas time to embark,
Persuaded the creatures to enter the Ark,
The dog, with a friendliness truly sublime,
Assisted in herding them. Two at a time
He drove in the elephants, zebras and gnus
Until they were packed like a boxful of screws,
The cat in the cupboard, the mouse on the shelf,
The bug in the crack; then he backed in himself.
But such was the lack of available space
He couldn't tuck all of him into the place;
So after the waters had flooded the plain
And down from the heavens fell blankets of rain
He stood with his muzzle thrust out through the door
The whole forty days of that terrible pour!
Because of which drenching, zoologists hold,
The nose of a healthy dog always is cold!

Arthur Guiterman, *Lyric Laughter*
Copyright 1939 by E. P. Dutton & Co., Inc., New York
By permission of the publishers

KINDNESS TO ANIMALS

Riddle cum diddle cum dido,
My little dog's name is Fido;
   I bought him a wagon,
   And hitched up a dragon,
And off we both went for a ride, oh!

Riddle cum diddle cum doodle,
My little cat's name is Toodle;
   I curled up her hair,
   But she only said, "There!
You have made me look *just* like a poodle!"

Riddle cum diddle cum dinky,
My little pig's name is Winkie;
   I keep him quite clean
   With the washing machine,
And I rinse him all off in the sinkie.

Laura E. Richards, *Tirra Lirra*

MY DONKEY

(French)

My donkey, my dear,
Had a pain in his head;
A kind lady gave him
A bonnet of red,
And little shoes of lavender,
Lav—lav—lavender,
And little shoes of lavender
To keep him from the cold.

My donkey, my dear,
Had a pain in his throat;
A kind lady gave him
A button-up coat,
And little shoes of lavender,
Lav—lav—lavender,
And little shoes of lavender
To keep him from the cold.

My donkey, my dear,
Had a pain in his chest;
A kind lady gave him
A thick woolly vest,
And little shoes of lavender,
Lav—lav—lavender,
And little shoes of lavender,
To keep him from the cold.

Rose Fyleman, *Picture Rhymes from Foreign Lands*

THE PURPLE COW

I never saw a Purple Cow,
  I never hope to see one;
But I can tell you, anyhow,
  I'd rather see than be one.

Gelett Burgess, *The Burgess Nonsense Book*
J. B. Lippincott Company, New York, 1901

How much wood would a wood-chuck chuck
If a wood-chuck could chuck wood?
He would chuck as much wood as a wood-chuck would chuck,
If a wood-chuck could chuck wood.

The American Mother Goose (Compiled by Ray Wood)
Copyright 1940 by J. B. Lippincott Company

A flea and a fly in a flue
Were imprisoned, so what could they do?
  Said the fly, "Let us flee,"
  Said the flea, "Let us fly,"
So they flew through a flaw in the flue.

Unknown

ONLY MY OPINION

Is a caterpillar ticklish?
  Well, it's always my belief
That he giggles, as he wiggles
  Across a hairy leaf.

Monica Shannon, *Goose Grass Rhymes*
Copyright 1930 by Doubleday & Company, Inc.

A CENTIPEDE

A centipede was happy quite,
Until a frog in fun
Said, "Pray, which leg comes after which?"
This raised her mind to such a pitch,
She lay distracted in a ditch,
Considering how to run.

Unknown

THE OSTRICH IS A SILLY BIRD

The ostrich is a silly bird,
 With scarcely any mind.
He often runs so very fast,
 He leaves himself behind.

And when he gets there, has to stand
 And hang about till night,
Without a blessed thing to do
 Until he comes in sight.

Mary E. Wilkins Freeman
In *Harper's Magazine*, August 1905
By permission of the publishers

THE BUMBLEBEAVER

A cheerful and industrious beast,
 He's always humming as he goes
To make mud-houses with his tail
 Or gather honey with his nose.

Although he flits from flower to flower
 He's not at all a gay deceiver.
We might take lessons by the hour
 From busy, buzzy Bumblebeaver.

Kenyon Cox, *Mixed Beasts*
Reprinted by permission of Dodd, Mead & Company

ANTELOPE

When he takes a bath, the Antelope
Uses lots of water and little soap;
Then he shakes himself dry and runs up the slope
As clean as a whistle—or so I hope.

Up the bank quickly the Antelope goes
And on the tall grass he rubs his wet nose.
Down from his ears the cool water flows;
He runs up the bank—and away he goes!

William Jay Smith, *Boy Blue's Book of Beasts*
Copyright © 1956, 1957 by William Jay Smith
By permission of the author
and publisher, Little, Brown & Company, Boston

SOME FISHY
NONSENSE

Timothy Tiggs and Tomothy Toggs,
They both went a-fishing for pollothywogs;
   They both went a-fishing
   Because they were wishing
To see how the creatures would turn into frogs.

Timothy Tiggs and Tomothy Toggs,
They both got stuck in the bogothybogs;
   They caught a small minnow,
   And said 't was a sin oh!
That things with no legs should pretend to be frogs.

Laura E. Richards, *Tirra Lirra*
Little, Brown & Company, Boston, 1932

ALAS, ALACK!

Ann, Ann!
   Come! Quick as you can!
There's a fish that *talks*
   In the frying-pan.
Out of the fat,
   As clear as glass,
He put up his mouth
   And moaned "Alas!"
Oh, most mournful,
   "Alas, alack!"
Then turned to his sizzling,
   And sank him back.

Walter de la Mare, *Collected Poems, 1901–1918*
Copyright 1920 by Henry Holt and Company, Inc.
Copyright 1948 by Walter de la Mare
Reprinted by permission of the publishers
(Also in *Rhymes and Verses* by Walter de la Mare
Published by Henry Holt and Company, Inc., New York, 1947)

The cow has a cud
The turtle has mud
The rabbit has a hutch
But I haven't much

The ox has a yoke
The frog has a croak
The toad has a wart
So he's not my sort

The mouse has a hole
The polecat a pole
The goose has a hiss
And it goes like this

The duck has a pond
The bird has beyond
The hen has a chick
But I feel sick

The horse has hay
The dog has his day
The bee has a sting
And a queen not a king

The robin has a worm
The worm has a squirm
The squirrel has a nut
Every wheel has a rut

The pig has a pen
The bear has a den
The trout has a pool
While I have school

The crow has a nest
The hawk has a quest
The owl has a mate
Doggone! I'm late!

FROM
ODDITY
LAND

I know seven mice
That go skating on ice.
One doesn't like it and six think it's nice.

I know a raccoon
That can whistle a tune,
But only on Tuesdays when there's a full moon.

I know an ox
That always wears socks.
He's specially fond of the ones that have clocks.

I know a whale
That receives lots of mail.
He opens it up with a flick of his tail.

THERE

ONCE

WAS A

PUFFIN

Oh, there once was a Puffin
Just the shape of a muffin,
And he lived on an island
In the
    bright
      blue
        sea!

He ate little fishes,
That were most delicious,
And he had them for supper
And he
    had
      them
        for tea.

But this poor little Puffin,
He couldn't play nothin',
For he hadn't anybody
To
    play
      with
        at all.

So he sat on his island,
And he cried for awhile, and
He felt very lonely,
And he
    felt
      very
        small.

Then along came the fishes,
And they said, "If you wishes,

276

You can have us for playmates,
Instead
        of
            for
                tea!"

So they now play together,
In all sorts of weather,
And the Puffin eats pancakes,
Like you
        and
            like
                me.

Florence Page Jaques
In *Child Life*, January 1930
Copyright 1930 by Rand McNally & Company
By permission of the author

THREE LITTLE PUFFINS

Three little puffins
Were partial to muffins,
As partial as partial can be.
They wouldn't eat nuffin
But hot buttered muffin
For breakfast and dinner and tea.
Pantin' and puffin'
And chewin' and chuffin'
They just went on stuffin', dear me!
Till the three little puffins
Were chockful of muffins
And puffy as puffy can be,
                All three
Were puffy as puffy can be.

Eleanor Farjeon, *The Silver Curlew*
Copyright 1953 by Eleanor Farjeon
By permission of the author
and publisher, The Viking Press, Inc., New York

THE OCTOPUS

Tell me, O Octopus, I begs,
Is those things arms, or is they legs?
I marvel at thee, Octopus;
If I were thou, I'd call me Us.

Ogden Nash, *Good Intentions*
Copyright 1942 by Ogden Nash
By permission of Little, Brown & Co.

**THE
OCTOPUSSYCAT**

I love Octopussy, his arms are so long;
There's nothing in nature so sweet as his song.
'Tis true I'd not touch him—no, not for a farm!
If I keep at a distance he'll do me no harm.

Kenyon Cox, *Mixed Beasts*
Reprinted by permission of Dodd, Mead & Company

**HABITS
OF THE
HIPPOPOTAMUS**

The hippopotamus is strong
  And huge of head and broad of bustle;
The limbs on which he rolls along
  Are big with hippopotomuscle.

He does not greatly care for sweets
  Like ice cream, apple pie, or custard,
But takes to flavor what he eats
  A little hippopotomustard.

The hippopotamus is true
  To all his principles, and just;
He always tries his best to do
  The things one hippopotomust.

278

He never rides in trucks or trams,
In taxicabs or omnibuses,
And so keeps out of traffic jams
And other hippopotomusses.

Arthur Guiterman, *Gaily the Troubadour*
Copyright 1936 by E. P. Dutton & Co., Inc., New York
By permission of the publishers

How doth the little crocodile
Improve his shining tail,
And pour the waters of the Nile
On every golden scale!

How cheerfully he seems to grin,
How neatly spreads his claws,
And welcomes little fishes in,
With gently smiling jaws!

Lewis Carroll

"The time has come," the Walrus said,
"To talk of many things:
Of shoes—and ships—and sealing-wax—
Of cabbages—and kings—
And why the sea is boiling hot—
And whether pigs have wings."

Lewis Carroll

SO MANY MONKEYS

Monkey Monkey Moo!
Shall we buy a few?
Yellow monkeys,
Purple monkeys,
Monkeys red and blue.

Be a monkey, do!
Who's a monkey, *who?*
He's a monkey,
She's a monkey,
You're a monkey, too!

Marion Edey and Dorothy Grider, *Open the Door*
Copyright 1949 by Marion Edey and Dorothy Grider
Reprinted by permission of the publishers, Charles Scribner's Sons

MONKEY

High on a banyan tree in a row
Sat three black Monkeys when it started to snow.
The first Monkey lifted his paw and said:
"I think I must have a cold in the head;
Though snow in a jungle just cannot be,
That certainly looks like snow to me."
The second exclaimed: "I would also
Be inclined to say that it was snow;
But there may be something wrong with me."
Third Monkey—wisest of the three—
Cried, "Look!" and pointed high in the tree.
A fourth Monkey stood there shaking a vine
Heavy with blossoms white and fine
Which fell through the air like flakes of snow
On the upturned faces there below—
And continued to fall till the jungle green
Was changed into a winter scene,
And huge white petals without sound
Had swept in drifts across the ground.

William Jay Smith, *Boy Blue's Book of Beasts*
Copyright © 1956, 1957 by William Jay Smith
By permission of the author
and publisher, Little, Brown & Company, Boston

THE MONKEYS AND THE CROCODILE

Five little monkeys
  Swinging from a tree;
Teasing Uncle Crocodile,
  Merry as can be.
Swinging high, swinging low,
  Swinging left and right:
"Dear Uncle Crocodile,
  Come and take a bite!"

Five little monkeys
  Swinging in the air;
Heads up, tails up,
  Little do they care.
Swinging up, swinging down,
  Swinging far and near:
"Poor Uncle Crocodile,
  Aren't you hungry, dear?"

Four little monkeys
  Sitting in the tree;
Heads down, tails down,
  Dreary as can be.
Weeping loud, weeping low,
  Crying to each other:
"Wicked Uncle Crocodile,
  To gobble up our brother!"

Laura E. Richards, *Tirra Lirra*
Little, Brown & Company, Boston, 1932

THE

SHIP

OF RIO

There was a ship of Rio
  Sailed out into the blue,
And nine and ninety monkeys
  Were all her jovial crew.
From bo'sun to the cabin boy,
  From quarter to caboose,
There weren't a stitch of calico
  To breech 'em—tight or loose;
From spar to deck, from deck to keel,
  From barnacle to shroud,
There weren't one pair of reach-me-downs
  To all that jabbering crowd.
But wasn't it a gladsome sight,
  When roared the deep-sea gales,
To see them reef her fore and aft,
  A-swinging by their tails!
Oh, wasn't it a gladsome sight,
  When glassy calm did come,
To see them squatting tailor-wise
  Around a keg of rum!
Oh, wasn't it a gladsome sight,
  When in she sailed to land,
To see them all a-scampering skip
  For nuts across the sand!

Walter de la Mare, *Collected Poems, 1901–1918*

ZEBRA

Are zebras black with broad white stripes,
Or are they really white with black?
Answer me that and I'll give you some candy
And a green-and-yellow jumping jack.

William Jay Smith, *Boy Blue's Book of Beasts*

THE PANTHER

The panther is like a leopard,
Except it hasn't been peppered.
Should you behold a panther crouch,
Prepare to say Ouch.
Better yet, if called by a panther,
Don't anther.

Ogden Nash, *Many Long Years Ago*
Copyright 1936, 1940 by Ogden Nash
By permission of the author
and publisher, Little, Brown & Company, Boston

YAK

The long-haired Yak has long black hair,
He lets it grow—he doesn't care.
He lets it grow and grow and grow,
He lets it trail along the stair.
Does he ever go to the barbershop? NO!
How wild and woolly and devil-may-care
A long-haired Yak with long black hair
Would look when perched in a barber chair!

William Jay Smith, *Boy Blue's Book of Beasts*
Copyright © 1956, 1957 by William Jay Smith
By permission of the author
and publisher, Little, Brown & Company, Boston

THE KANGAROOSTER

His tail is remarkably long
And his legs are remarkably strong;
But the strength and the length of his legs and his tail
Are as naught to the strength of his song.

He picks up his food with his bill;
He bounds over valley and hill;
But the height of his bounds can't compare with the sounds
He lets out when he crows with a will.

Kenyon Cox, *Mixed Beasts*
Reprinted by permission of Dodd, Mead & Company

FURRY BEAR

If I were a bear,
  And a big bear too,
I shouldn't much care
  If it froze or snew;
I shouldn't much mind
  If it snowed or friz—
I'd be all fur-lined
  With a coat like his!

For I'd have fur boots and a brown fur wrap,
And brown fur knickers and a big fur cap.
I'd have a fur muffle-ruff to cover my jaws,
And brown fur mittens on my big brown paws.
With a big brown furry-down up to my head,
I'd sleep all the winter in a big fur bed.

A. A. Milne, *Now We Are Six*

GRIZZLY BEAR

If you ever, ever, ever meet a grizzly bear,
You must never, never, never ask him *where*
He is going,
Or *what* he is doing;
For if you ever, ever, dare
To stop a grizzly bear,
You will never meet *another* grizzly bear.

Mary Austin, *The Children Sing in the Far West*

A TIGER'S TALE

There was an ancient Grecian boy
Who played upon the fiddle,
Sometimes high, sometimes low,
Sometimes in the middle;
And all day long beneath the shade
He lunched on prunes and marmalade;
But what the tunes were which he played
  Is certainly a riddle.

Three tigers, gaunt and ravenous,
Came from the gloomy wood,
Intent to slay the fiddler,
But his music was too good;
So round about him once they filed,
Till by the melody beguiled,
They sat them softly down and smiled,
  As only tigers could.

And thus beguiled, the tigers smiled
Throughout the livelong day
Until, at length, there was not left
  Another tune to play.

What happened then I do not know
I was not there to see.
But when a man runs short on tunes,
Can tigers be appeased with prunes,
Or marmalade and silver spoons?
  That's what perplexes me.

John Bennett

HOW TO TELL THE WILD ANIMALS

If ever you should go by chance
    To jungles in the East;
And if there should to you advance
    A large and tawny beast,
If he roars at you as you're dyin'
You'll know it is the Asian Lion.

Or if some time when roaming round,
    A noble wild beast greets you,
With black stripes on a yellow ground,
    Just notice if he eats you.
This simple rule may help you learn
The Bengal Tiger to discern.

If strolling forth, a beast you view,
    Whose hide with spots is peppered,
As soon as he has lept on you,
    You'll know it is the Leopard.
'Twill do no good to roar with pain,
He'll only lep and lep again.

If when you're walking round your yard,
    You meet a creature there,
Who hugs you very, very hard,
    Be sure it is the Bear.
If you have any doubt, I guess
He'll give you just one more caress.

Though to distinguish beasts of prey
    A novice might nonplus,
The Crocodiles you always may
    Tell from Hyenas thus:
Hyenas come with merry smiles;
But if they weep, they're Crocodiles.

The true Chameleon is small,
    A lizard sort of thing;
He hasn't any ears at all,
    And not a single wing.
If there is nothing on the tree,
'Tis the Chameleon you see.

Carolyn Wells, *Baubles*
Reprinted by permission of Dodd, Mead & Company

 I asked my mother for fifteen cents
To see the elephant jump the fence,
He jumped so high that he touched the sky
And never came back 'till the Fourth of July.

The American Mother Goose (Compiled by Ray Wood)
Copyright 1940 by J. B. Lippincott Company

ELETELEPHONY

Once there was an elephant,
Who tried to use the telephant—
No! no! I mean an elephone
Who tried to use the telephone—
(Dear me! I am not certain quite
That even now I've got it right.)

Howe'er it was, he got his trunk
Entangled in the telephunk;
The more he tried to get it free,
The louder buzzed the telephee—
(I fear I'd better drop the song
Of elephop and telephong!)

Laura E. Richards, *Tirra Lirra*
Copyright 1918, 1930, 1932 by Laura E. Richards
By permission of Little, Brown & Co.

THE FOUR FRIENDS

Ernest was an elephant, a great big fellow,
  Leonard was a lion with a six-foot tail,
George was a goat, and his beard was yellow,
      And James was a very small snail.

Leonard had a stall, and a great big strong one,
  Ernest had a manger, and its walls were thick,
George found a pen, but I think it was the wrong one,
      And James sat down on a brick.

Ernest started trumpeting, and cracked his manger,
  Leonard started roaring, and shivered his stall,
James gave the huffle of a snail in danger
      And nobody heard him at all.

Ernest started trumpeting and raised such a rumpus,
  Leonard started roaring and trying to kick,
James went a journey with the goat's new compass
      And he reached the end of his brick.

Ernest was an elephant and very well-intentioned,
  Leonard was a lion with a brave new tail,
George was a goat, as I think I have mentioned,
      But James was only a snail.

A. A. Milne, *When We Were Very Young*

AT THE ZOO

There are lions and roaring tigers, and enormous camels and things,
There are biffalo-buffalo-bisons, and a great big bear with wings,
There's a sort of a tiny potamus, and a tiny nosserus too—
But *I* gave buns to the elephant when *I* went down to the Zoo!

There are badgers and bidgers and bodgers, and a Super-intendent's
     House,
There are masses of goats, and a Polar, and different kinds of mouse,
And I think there's a sort of a something which is called a wallaboo—
But *I* gave buns to the elephant when *I* went down to the Zoo!

If you try to talk to the bison, he never quite understands;
You can't shake hands with a mingo—he doesn't like shaking hands.
And lions and roaring tigers *hate* saying, "How do you do?"—
But *I* give buns to the elephant when *I* go down to the Zoo!

A. A. Milne, *When We Were Very Young*

THE SPANGLED PANDEMONIUM

The Spangled Pandemonium
Is missing from the zoo.
He bent the bars the barest bit,
And slithered glibly through.

He crawled across the moated wall,
He climbed the mango tree,
And when his keeper scrambled up,
He nipped him in the knee.

To all of you, a warning
Not to wander after dark,
Or if you must, make very sure
You stay out of the park.

For the Spangled Pandemonium
Is missing from the zoo,
And since he nipped his keeper,
He would just as soon nip you!

Palmer Brown, *Beyond the Paw Paw Trees*
Copyright 1954 by Palmer Brown
Published by Harper & Brothers, New York

JABBERWOCKY

'Twas brillig, and the slithy toves
  Did gyre and gimble in the wabe:
All mimsy were the borogoves,
    And the mome raths outgrabe.

"Beware the Jabberwock, my son!
  The jaws that bite, the claws that catch!
Beware the Jubjub bird, and shun
    The frumious Bandersnatch!"

He took his vorpal sword in hand:
  Long time the manxome foe he sought—
So rested he by the Tumtum tree,
    And stood awhile in thought.

And, as in uffish thought he stood,
  The Jabberwock, with eyes of flame,
Came whiffling through the tulgey wood,
    And burbled as it came!

One, two! One, two! And through and through
  The vorpal blade went snicker-snack!
He left it dead, and with its head
    He went galumphing back.

"And hast thou slain the Jabberwock?
  Come to my arms, my beamish boy!
O frabjous day! Callooh! Callay!"
    He chortled in his joy.

'Twas brillig, and the slithy toves
  Did gyre and gimble in the wabe:
All mimsy were the borogoves,
    And the mome raths outgrabe.

Lewis Carroll

Mary, Mary, quite contrary,
 How does your garden grow?
Silver bells and cockle-shells,
 And pretty maids all of a row.

Mother Goose

LUCY LOCKET

Lucy Locket lost her pocket,
 Kitty Fisher found it;
Not a penny was there in it,
 Only ribbon round it.

Mother Goose

Peter, Peter, pumpkin-eater,
Had a wife and couldn't keep her;
He put her in a pumpkin shell,
And there he kept her very well.

Mother Goose

Little Boy Blue, come blow your horn;
The sheep's in the meadow, the cow's in the corn.
Where's the little boy that looks after the sheep?
 He's under the haystack, fast asleep.

Mother Goose

Wee Willie Winkie runs through the town,
Upstairs and downstairs, in his nightgown;
Rapping at the window, crying through the lock,
 "Are the children in their beds?
 Now it's eight o'clock."

Mother Goose

Jack and Jill went up the hill
 To fetch a pail of water.
Jack fell down and broke his crown
 And Jill came tumbling after.

Up Jack got and home he did trot
 As fast as he could caper.
He went to bed to mend his head
 In vinegar and brown paper.

Mother Goose

Little Miss Muffet
 Sat on a tuffet,
Eating of curds and whey;
 There came a big spider,
 And sat down beside her,
And frightened Miss Muffet away.

Mother Goose

Little Bo-Peep has lost her sheep,
And can't tell where to find them;
Leave them alone, and they'll come home,
And bring their tails behind them.

Little Bo-Peep fell fast asleep,
And dreamt she heard them bleating;
But when she awoke, she found it a joke,
For still they all were fleeting.

Then up she took her little crook,
Determined for to find them;
She found them indeed, but it made her heart bleed,
For they'd left all their tails behind 'em!

It happened one day, as Bo-Peep did stray
Unto a meadow hard by—
There she espied their tails, side by side,
All hung on a tree to dry.

She heaved a sigh and wiped her eye,
And over the hillocks she raced;
And tried what she could, as a shepherdess should,
That each tail should be properly placed.

Mother Goose

PETER PIPER

Peter Piper picked a peck of pickled peppers;
A peck of pickled peppers Peter Piper picked;
If Peter Piper picked a peck of pickled peppers,
Where's the peck of pickled peppers Peter Piper picked?

Mother Goose

 Ding, dong, bell!
Pussy's in the well!
   Who put her in?
Little Johnny Green.
   Who pulled her out?
Little Johnny Stout.

   What a naughty boy was that
To try to drown poor pussy cat
   Which never did him any harm,
But killed the mice in his father's barn!

Mother Goose

OLD MOTHER HUBBARD

Old Mother Hubbard
Went to the cupboard,
To fetch her poor dog a bone;
But when she came there
The cupboard was bare
And so the poor dog had none.

She went to the baker's
To buy him some bread;
But when she came back
The poor dog was dead.

She went to the undertaker's
To buy him a coffin;
But when she came back
The poor dog was laughing.

She took a clean dish
To get him some tripe;
But when she came back
He was smoking a pipe.

She went to the alehouse
To get him some beer;
But when she came back
The dog sat in a chair.

She went to the tavern
For white wine and red;
But when she came back
The dog stood on his head.

She went to the fruiterer's
To buy him some fruit;
But when she came back
He was playing the flute.

She went to the tailor's
  To buy him a coat;
But when she came back
  He was riding a goat.

She went to the hatter's
  To buy him a hat;
But when she came back
  He was feeding the cat.

She went to the barber's
  To buy him a wig;
But when she came back
  He was dancing a jig.

She went to the cobbler's
  To buy him some shoes;
But when she came back
  He was reading the news.

She went to the seamstress
  To buy him some linen;
But when she came back
  The dog was a-spinning.

She went to the hosier's
  To buy him some hose;
But when she came back
  He was dressed in his clothes.

The dame made a curtsy,
  The dog made a bow;
The dame said, Your servant,
  The dog said, Bow-wow.

Mother Goose

A diller, a dollar, a ten o'clock scholar!
　What makes you come so soon?
You used to come at ten o'clock,
　But now you come at noon.

Mother Goose

Bye, baby bunting,
Father's gone a-hunting,
Mother's gone a-milking,
　Sister's gone a-silking,
And brother's gone to buy a skin
To wrap the baby bunting in.

Mother Goose

ROCK-A-BYE

BABY

Rock-a-bye, baby, on the tree-top,
When the wind blows, the cradle will rock;
When the bough breaks the cradle will fall,
And down will come baby, cradle and all.

Mother Goose

I know a barber
Whose shop's in an arbor
A mile and a quarter from Oddity Harbor.
He caters to goats who have beards to their knees,
For his favorite hobby is trimming goatees.

Edward Anthony, *Oddity Land*

298

There was an old woman who lived in a shoe;
She had so many children she didn't know what to do;
She gave them some broth without any bread;
She whipped them all soundly and put them to bed.

Mother Goose

Hark, hark! the dogs do bark!
   Beggars are coming to town:
Some in jags, and some in rags,
   And some in velvet gown.

Mother Goose

There was an old man named Michael Finnegan,
He grew a long beard right on his chinnigan,
Along came a wind and blew it in again—
Poor old Michael Finnegan.

The American Mother Goose (Compiled by Ray Wood)
Copyright 1940 by J. B. Lippincott Company

There was a Young Lady of Niger
Who smiled as she rode on a tiger;
   They returned from the ride
   With the lady inside,
And the smile on the face of the tiger.

Cosmo Monkhouse

There was an old woman, as I've heard tell,
She went to market her eggs to sell;
She went to market all on a market-day,
And she fell asleep on the king's highway.

There came by a peddler whose name was Stout;
He cut her petticoats all round about;
He cut her petticoats up to the knees,
Which made the old woman to shiver and freeze.

When this little woman first did wake,
She began to shiver and she began to shake;
She began to wonder and she began to cry,
"Oh! deary, deary me, this is none of I!

"But if it be I, as I do hope it be,
I've a little dog at home, and he'll know me;
If it be I, he'll wag his little tail,
And if it be not I, he'll loudly bark and wail."

Home went the little woman all in the dark;
Up got the little dog, and he began to bark;
He began to bark, so she began to cry,
"Oh! deary, deary me, this is none of I!"

Mother Goose

There was a Young Lady whose chin
Resembled the point of a pin;
So she had it made sharp, and purchased a harp,
And played several tunes with her chin.

Edward Lear

A tutor who tooted a flute
Tried to teach two young tutors to toot.
  Said the two to the tutor,
  "Is it harder to toot, or
To tutor two tutors to toot?"

Carolyn Wells

There was an Old Man with a beard,
Who said, "It is just as I feared!—
Two Owls and a Hen, four Larks and a Wren,
Have all built their nests in my beard."

Edward Lear

There was a Young Lady of Norway,
Who casually sat in a doorway;
When the door squeezed her flat,
    she exclaimed, "What of that?"
This courageous Young Lady of Norway.

Edward Lear

JONATHAN

(Dutch)

Jonathan Gee
Went out with his cow;
He climbed up a tree
And sat on a bough.
He sat on a bough
And it broke in half,
And John's old cow
Did nothing but laugh.

Rose Fyleman, *Picture Rhymes from Foreign Lands*
Copyright 1935 by Rose Fyleman
Reprinted by permission of J. B. Lippincott Company

Tommy was a silly boy,
  "I can fly," he said;
He started off, but very soon,
  He tumbled on his head.

His little sister Prue was there,
  To see how he would do it;
She knew that, after all his boast,
  Full dearly Tom would rue it!

Kate Greenaway, *Under the Window*
Frederick Warne and Company, New York and London, 1910

TIMOTHY BOON

Timothy Boon
Bought a balloon
Blue as the sky,
Round as the moon.
"Now I will try
To make it fly
Up to the moon,
Higher than high!"
Timothy said,
Nodding his head.

Timothy Boon
Sent his balloon
Up through the skies,
Up to the moon.
But a strong breeze
Stirred in the trees,
Rocked the bright moon,
Tossed the great seas,
And, with its mirth,
Shook the whole earth.

Timothy Boon,
And his balloon,
Caught by the breeze
Flew to the moon;
Up past the trees,
Over the seas,
Up to the moon—
Swift as you please!—
And, ere I forget,
They have not come down yet!

Ivy O. Eastwick, *Fairies and Suchlike*
Published and copyright 1946 by E. P. Dutton & Co., Inc., New York

THE STORY OF AUGUSTUS

Augustus was a chubby lad;
Fat ruddy cheeks Augustus had;
And every body saw with joy
The plump and hearty healthy boy.
He ate and drank as he was told,
And never let his soup get cold.
But one day, one cold winter's day,
He scream'd out—"Take the soup away!
O take the nasty soup away!
I won't have any soup to-day."

Next day, now look, the picture shows
How lank and lean Augustus grows!
Yet, though he feels so weak and ill,
The naughty fellow cries out still—
"Not any soup for me, I say:
O take the nasty soup away!
I won't have any soup to-day."

The third day comes; Oh what a sin!
To make himself so pale and thin.
Yet, when the soup is put on table,
He screams, as loud as he is able,—
"Not any soup for me, I say:
O take the nasty soup away!
I won't have any soup to-day."

Look at him, now the fourth day's come!
He scarcely weighs a sugar-plum;
He's like a little bit of thread,
And on the fifth day, he was—dead!

Heinrich Hoffmann, *Slovenly Peter*

GODFREY GORDON GUSTAVUS GORE

Godfrey Gordon Gustavus Gore—
No doubt you have heard the name before—
Was a boy who never would shut a door!

The wind might whistle, the wind might roar,
And teeth be aching and throats be sore,
But still he never would shut the door.

His father would beg, his mother implore,
"Godfrey Gordon Gustavus Gore,
We really *do* wish you would shut the door!"

Their hands they wrung, their hair they tore;
But Godfrey Gordon Gustavus Gore
Was deaf as the buoy out at the Nore.

When he walked forth the folks would roar,
"Godfrey Gordon Gustavus Gore,
Why don't you think to shut the door?"

They rigged out a Shutter with sail and oar,
And threatened to pack off Gustavus Gore
On a voyage of penance to Singapore.

But he begged for mercy, and said, "No more!
Pray do not send me to Singapore
On a Shutter, and then I will shut the door!"

"You will?" said his parents; "then keep on shore!
But mind you do! For the plague is sore
Of a fellow that never will shut the door,
Godfrey Gordon Gustavus Gore!"

William Brighty Rands

THE STORY OF JOHNNY HEAD-IN-AIR

As he trudg'd along to school,
It was always Johnny's rule
To be looking at the sky
And the clouds that floated by;
But what just before him lay,
In his way,
Johnny never thought about;
So that every one cried out—
"Look at little Johnny there,
Little Johnny Head-in-Air!"

Running just in Johnny's way,
Came a little dog one day;
Johnny's eyes were still astray
Up on high,
In the sky;
And he never heard them cry—
"Johnny, mind, the dog is nigh!"
Bump!
Dump!
Down they fell, with such a thump,
Dog and Johnny in a lump!

Once, with head as high as ever,
Johnny walk'd beside the river.
Johnny watch'd the swallows trying
Which was cleverest at flying.
Oh! what fun!
Johnny watch'd the bright round sun
Going in and coming out;
This was all he thought about.
So he strode on, only think!
To the river's very brink,

Where the bank was high and steep,
And the water very deep;
And the fishes, in a row,
Stared to see him coming so.

One step more! Oh! sad to tell!
Headlong in poor Johnny fell.
And the fishes, in dismay,
Wagg'd their tails and ran away.

There lay Johnny on his face,
With his nice red writing-case;
But, as they were passing by,
Two strong men had heard him cry;
And, with sticks, these two strong men
Hook'd poor Johnny out again.
Oh! you should have seen him shiver
When they pull'd him from the river.
He was in a sorry plight!
Dripping wet, and such a fright!
Wet all over, everywhere,
Clothes, and arms, and face, and hair;
Johnny never will forget
What it is to be so wet.

And the fishes, one, two, three,
All came back again, you see,
Up they came the moment after,
To enjoy the fun and laughter.
Each popp'd out his little head,
And, to tease poor Johnny, said,
"Silly little Johnny, look,
You have lost your writing-book!"

Heinrich Hoffmann, *Slovenly Peter*

307

STATELY VERSE

If Mary goes far out to sea,
  By wayward breezes fanned,
I'd like to know—can you tell me?—
  Just where would Maryland?

If Tenny went high up in air
  And looked o'er land and lea,
Looked here and there and everywhere,
  Pray what would Tennessee?

I looked out of the window and
  Saw Orry on the lawn;
He's not there now, and who can tell
  Just where has Oregon?

Two girls were quarrelling one day
  With garden tools, and so
I said, "My dears, let Mary rake
  And just let Idaho."

A friend of mine lived in a flat
  With half a dozen boys;
When he fell ill I asked him why.
  He said: "I'm Illinois."

An English lady had a steed.
  She called him 'Ighland Bay.
She rode for exercise, and thus
  Rhode Island every day.

Unknown

ANTONIO

Antonio, Antonio,
Was tired of living alonio.
  He thought he would woo
  Miss Lissamy Lou,
Miss Lissamy Lucy Molonio.

Antonio, Antonio,
Rode off on his polo-ponio.
  He found the fair maid
  In a bowery shade,
A-sitting and knitting alonio.

Antonio, Antonio,
Said, "If you will be my ownio,
  I'll love you true,
  And I'll buy for you,
An icery creamery conio!"

"Oh, nonio, Antonio!
You're far too bleak and bonio!
  And all that I wish,
  You singular fish,
Is that you will quickly begonio."

Antonio, Antonio,
He uttered a dismal moanio;
  Then ran off and hid
  (Or I'm told that he did)
In the Antarctical Zonio.

Laura E. Richards

JOHN HENRY

When John Henry was about three days old,
    A-sittin' on his pappy's knee,
He gave-a one long loud and-a lonesome cry,
    Said, "Dat hammer'll be the death of me."

Now John Henry said to his Captain one day,
    "A man ain't nothing but a man,
But before I'll be governed by an old steam drill,
    I'll die with my hammer in my hand."

Now John Henry swung his hammer around of his head
    And brought his hammer down on the ground.
A man in Chattanooga, two hundred miles away,
    Heard an awful rumbling sound.

Now John Henry had a pretty little gal,
    Her name was Polly Anne.
When John Henry was sick and a-layin' on his bed,
    Polly drove steel like a man.

When John Henry died, they wasn't no box
    Big enough to hold his bones,
So they buried him in a box-car deep in the ground,
    And let two mountains be his grave-stones.

Traditional: American

Adapted by John Jacob Niles in *More Songs of the Hill Folk*
Published and copyright 1936 by G. Schirmer, Inc., New York
By permission of the publisher

MOMOTARA

(*Japanese*)

Where did Momotara go,
With a hoity-toity-tighty?
He went to lay the giants low,
The wicked ones and mighty.

What did Momotara take?
His monkey, dog and pheasant,
Some dumplings and an almond cake,
Which made the journey pleasant.

How did Momotara fare
Upon the fearful meeting?
He seized the giants by the hair
And gave them all a beating.

What did Momotara bring?
Oh, more than you could measure:
A silver coat, a golden ring
And a waggon-load of treasure.

What did Momotara do?
He sat himself astride it;
The monkey pushed, the pheasant drew
And the little dog ran beside it.

Rose Fyleman, *Picture Rhymes from Foreign Lands*

AMBITION

When I am grown an *hombre*
I shall have another *nombre,*
They won't call me "Ramonito" any more;
But they'll call me *"caballero,"*
And I'll wave my wide *sombrero*
At all the señoritas I adore.

I've extravagant ideas:
Butter on all my *tortillas,*
And as much chokeberry jelly as I dare!
I will buy red combs for Mother—
She shall wear them, and no other—
With shiny stones to lie against her hair.

There will not be any, any,
That can use the words so many,
Or make speech so long as mine when I am big;
And for my songs I'll borrow
Uncle Pablo's good *guitarra.*—
But now I have to go and feed the pig.

Edith Agnew, *The Songs of Marcelino*
Ward Anderson Printing Company, Albuquerque, New Mexico, 1940

CURIOUS

SOMETHING

If I could smell smells with my ears,
    If sounds came buzzing in my nose,
If in my lips were looks and tears,
    Tongues in my eyes, do you suppose
        That I should have this kind of face,
        Or something curious in its place?

Winifred Welles, *Skipping Along Alone*
The Macmillan Company, New York, 1931

THE TWINS

In form and feature, face and limb,
    I grew so like my brother
That folks got taking me for him
    And each for one another.
It puzzled all our kith and kin,
    It reach'd an awful pitch;
For one of us was born a twin
    And not a soul knew which.

One day (to make the matter worse),
    Before our names were fix'd,
As we were being wash'd by nurse,
    We got completely mix'd.
And thus, you see, by Fate's decree,
    (Or rather nurse's whim),
My brother John got christen'd *me*,
    And I got christen'd *him*.

This fatal likeness even dogg'd
    My footsteps when at school,
And I was always getting flogg'd—
    For John turn'd out a fool.
I put this question hopelessly
    To every one I knew,—
What *would* you do, if you were me,
    To prove that you were *you?*

Our close resemblance turn'd the tide
    Of my domestic life;
For somehow my intended bride
    Became my brother's wife.
In short, year after year the same
    Absurd mistake went on;
And when I died—the neighbours came
    And buried brother John!

Henry Sambrooke Leigh

313

FELICIA
ROPPS

Funny, how Felicia Ropps
Always handles things in shops!
Always pinching, always poking,
Always feeling, always stroking
Things she has no right to touch!
Goops like that annoy me much!

Gelett Burgess, *Goop Directory*
J. B. Lippincott Company, New York, 1913

GOING
TOO
FAR

A woman who lived in Holland, of old,
Polished her brass till it shone like gold.
She washed her pig after all his meals
In spite of his energetic squeals.
She scrubbed her doorstep into the ground,
And the children's faces, pink and round,
She washed so hard that in several cases
She polished their features off their faces—
Which gave them an odd appearance, though
She thought they were really neater so!
Then her passion for cleaning quickly grew,
And she scrubbed and polished the village
    through,
Until, to the rage of all the people,
She cleaned the weather-vane off the steeple.
As she looked at the sky one summer's night
She thought that the stars shone out less bright;
And she said with a sigh, "If I were there,
I'd rub them up till the world should stare."
That night a storm began to brew,
And a wind from the ocean blew and blew
Till, when she came to her door next day
It whisked her up, and blew her away—

314

Up and up in the air so high
That she vanished, at last, in the stormy sky.
Since then it's said that each twinkling star
And the big white moon, shine brighter far.
But the neighbors shake their heads in fear
She may rub so hard they will disappear!

Mildred Howells
In *St. Nicholas*, March 1898
By permission of Juliet Lit Stern

MRS. SNIPKIN
AND MRS. WOBBLECHIN

Skinny Mrs. Snipkin,
  With her little pipkin,
Sat by the fireside a-warming of her toes.
  Fat Mrs. Wobblechin,
  With her little doublechin,
Sat by the window a-cooling of her nose.

  Says this one to that one,
  "Oh! you silly fat one,
Will you shut the window down? You're freezing me to death!"
  Says that one to t' other one,
  "Good gracious, how you bother one!
There isn't air enough for me to draw my precious breath!"

  Skinny Mrs. Snipkin,
  Took her little pipkin,
Threw it straight across the room as hard as she could throw;
  Hit Mrs. Wobblechin
  On her little doublechin,
And out of the window a-tumble she did go.

Laura E. Richards, *Tirra Lirra*
Little, Brown & Company, Boston, 1932

MR. PYME

Once upon a time
Old Mr. Pyme
Lived all alone
Under a stone.

When the rain fell
He rang a bell,
When the sun shined
He laughed and dined

And floated to town
On thistledown,
And what a nice time
Had Mr. Pyme!

Harry Behn, *The Little Hill*
Harcourt, Brace and Company, Inc., New York, Copyright 1949

JONATHAN

BING

Poor old Jonathan Bing
Went out in his carriage to visit the King,
But everyone pointed and said, "Look at that!
Jonathan Bing has forgotten his hat!"
(He'd forgotten his hat!)

Poor old Jonathan Bing
Went home and put on a new hat for the King,
But up by the palace a soldier said, "Hi!
You can't see the King; you've forgotten your tie!"
(He'd forgotten his tie!)

Poor old Jonathan Bing,
He put on a *beautiful* tie for the King,
But when he arrived an Archbishop said, "Ho!
You can't come to court in pyjamas, you know!"

Poor old Jonathan Bing
Went home and addressed a short note to the King:

> If you please will excuse me
> I won't come to tea;
> For home's the best place for
> All people like me!

Beatrice Curtis Brown, *Jonathan Bing and Other Verses*
Copyright 1936 by Beatrice Curtis Brown
Published by Oxford University Press, Inc., New York
By permission of the author

OLD QUIN QUEERIBUS

Old Quin Queeribus—
    He loved his garden so,
He wouldn't have a rake around,
    A shovel or a hoe.

For each potato's eyes he bought
    Fine spectacles of gold,
And mufflers for the corn, to keep
    Its ears from getting cold.

On every head of lettuce green—
    What do you think of that?—
And every head of cabbage, too,
    He tied a garden hat.

Old Quin Queeribus—
    He loved his garden so,
He couldn't eat his growing things,
    He only let them grow!

Nancy Byrd Turner, *Zodiac Town*
By permission of Little, Brown & Co.

317

THE TALE OF

CUSTARD THE DRAGON

Belinda lived in a little white house,
With a little black kitten and a little gray mouse,
And a little yellow dog and a little red wagon,
And a realio, trulio, little pet dragon.

Now the name of the little black kitten was Ink,
And the little gray mouse, she called her Blink,
And the little yellow dog was sharp as Mustard,
But the dragon was a coward, and she called him Custard.

Custard the dragon had big sharp teeth,
And spikes on top of him and scales underneath,
Mouth like a fireplace, chimney for a nose,
And realio, trulio daggers on his toes.

Belinda was as brave as a barrel full of bears,
And Ink and Blink chased lions down the stairs,
Mustard was as brave as a tiger in a rage,
But Custard cried for a nice safe cage.

Belinda tickled him, she tickled him unmerciful,
Ink, Blink and Mustard, they rudely called him Percival,
They all sat laughing in the little red wagon
At the realio, trulio, cowardly dragon.

Belinda giggled till she shook the house,
And Blink said Weeck! which is giggling for a mouse,
Ink and Mustard rudely asked his age,
When Custard cried for a nice safe cage.

Suddenly, suddenly they heard a nasty sound,
And Mustard growled, and they all looked around.
Meowch! cried Ink, and Ooh! cried Belinda,
For there was a pirate, climbing in the winda.

Pistol in his left hand, pistol in his right,
And he held in his teeth a cutlass bright,
His beard was black, one leg was wood;
It was clear that the pirate meant no good.

Belinda paled, and she cried Help! Help!
But Mustard fled with a terrified yelp,
Ink trickled down to the bottom of the household,
And little mouse Blink strategically mouseholed.

But up jumped Custard, snorting like an engine,
Clashed his tail like irons in a dungeon,
With a clatter and a clank and a jangling squirm
He went at the pirate like a robin at a worm.

The pirate gaped at Belinda's dragon,
And gulped some grog from his pocket flagon,
He fired two bullets, but they didn't hit,
And Custard gobbled him, every bit.

Belinda embraced him, Mustard licked him,
No one mourned for his pirate victim.
Ink and Blink in glee did gyrate
Around the dragon that ate the pyrate.

Belinda still lives in her little white house,
With her little black kitten and her little gray mouse,
And her little yellow dog and her little red wagon,
And her realio, trulio, little pet dragon.

Belinda is as brave as a barrel full of bears,
And Ink and Blink chase lions down the stairs,
Mustard is as brave as a tiger in a rage,
But Custard keeps crying for a nice safe cage.

Ogden Nash, *Many Long Years Ago*
Copyright 1936, 1940, by Ogden Nash
By permission of the author
and publisher, Little, Brown & Company, Boston

ADVENTURES

OF ISABEL

Isabel met an enormous bear,
Isabel, Isabel, didn't care;
The bear was hungry, the bear was ravenous,
The bear's big mouth was cruel and cavernous.
The bear said, Isabel, glad to meet you,
How do, Isabel, now I'll eat you!
Isabel, Isabel, didn't worry,
Isabel didn't scream or scurry.
She washed her hands and she straightened her hair up,
Then Isabel quietly ate the bear up.

Once in a night as black as pitch
Isabel met a wicked old witch.
The witch's face was cross and wrinkled,
The witch's gums with teeth were sprinkled.
Ho ho, Isabel! the old witch crowed,
I'll turn you into an ugly toad!
Isabel, Isabel, didn't worry,
Isabel didn't scream or scurry,
She showed no rage and she showed no rancor,
But she turned the witch into milk and drank her.

Isabel met a hideous giant,
Isabel continued self-reliant.
The giant was hairy, the giant was horrid,
He had one eye in the middle of his forehead.
Good morning Isabel, the giant said,
I'll grind your bones to make my bread.
Isabel, Isabel, didn't worry,
Isabel didn't scream or scurry.
She nibbled the zwieback that she always fed off,
And when it was gone, she cut the giant's head off.

Isabel met a troublesome doctor,
He punched and he poked till he really shocked her.
The doctor's talk was of coughs and chills
And the doctor's satchel bulged with pills.
The doctor said unto Isabel,
Swallow this, it will make you well.
Isabel, Isabel, didn't worry,
Isabel didn't scream or scurry.
She took those pills from the pill concocter,
And Isabel calmly cured the doctor.

Ogden Nash, *Many Long Years Ago*

Copyright 1936, 1940 by Ogden Nash
By permission of the author
and publisher, Little, Brown & Company, Boston

"You are old, Father William," the young man said,
  "And your hair has become very white;
And yet you incessantly stand on your head—
  Do you think, at your age, it is right?"

"In my youth," Father William replied to his son,
  "I feared it might injure the brain;
But, now that I'm perfectly sure I have none,
  Why, I do it again and again."

"You are old," said the youth, "as I mentioned before.
  And have grown most uncommonly fat;
Yet you turned a back-somersault in at the door—
  Pray, what is the reason of that?"

"In my youth," said the sage, as he shook his grey locks,
  "I kept all my limbs very supple
By the use of this ointment—one shilling the box—
  Allow me to sell you a couple?"

"You are old," said the youth, "and your jaws are too weak
    For anything tougher than suet;
Yet you finished the goose, with the bones and the beak—
    Pray, how did you manage to do it?"

"In my youth," said his father, "I took to the law,
    And argued each case with my wife;
And the muscular strength, which it gave to my jaw
    Has lasted the rest of my life."

"You are old," said the youth, "one would hardly suppose
    That your eye was as steady as ever;
Yet you balanced an eel on the end of your nose—
    What made you so awfully clever?"

"I have answered three questions, and that is enough,"
    Said his father. "Don't give yourself airs!
Do you think I can listen all day to such stuff?
    Be off, or I'll kick you down-stairs!"

                                                    Lewis Carroll

THE PIRATE
DON DURK
OF DOWDEE

Ho, for the Pirate Don Durk of Dowdee!
He was as wicked as wicked could be,
But oh, he was perfectly gorgeous to see!
    The Pirate Don Durk of Dowdee.

His conscience, of course, was as black as a bat,
But he had a floppety plume on his hat
And when he went walking it jiggled—like that!
    The plume of the Pirate Dowdee.

His coat it was crimson and cut with a slash,
And often as ever he twirled his mustache
Deep down in the ocean the mermaids went splash,
  Because of Don Durk of Dowdee.

Moreover, Dowdee had a purple tattoo,
And stuck in his belt where he buckled it through
Were a dagger, a dirk and a squizzamaroo,
  For fierce was the Pirate Dowdee.

So fearful he was he would shoot at a puff,
And always at sea when the weather grew rough
He drank from a bottle and wrote on his cuff,
  Did Pirate Don Durk of Dowdee.

Oh, he had a cutlass that swung at his thigh
And he had a parrot called Pepperkin Pye,
And a zigzaggy scar at the end of his eye
  Had Pirate Don Durk of Dowdee.

He kept in a cavern, this buccaneer bold,
A curious chest that was covered with mould,
And all of his pockets were jingly with gold!
  Oh jing! went the gold of Dowdee.

His conscience, of course, it was crook'd like a squash,
But both of his boots made a slickery slosh,
And he went through the world with a wonderful swash,
  Did Pirate Don Durk of Dowdee.

It's true he was wicked as wicked could be,
His sins they outnumbered a hundred and three,
But oh, he was perfectly gorgeous to see,
  The Pirate Don Durk of Dowdee.

Mildred Plew Meigs
In *Child Life*, March 1923
Copyright 1923 by Rand McNally & Company
By permission of Marion Plew Ruckel

THE

JUMBLIES

They went to sea in a sieve, they did;
   In a sieve they went to sea:
In spite of all their friends could say,
On a winter's morn, on a stormy day,
   In a sieve they went to sea.
And when the sieve turned round and round,
And every one cried, "You'll all be drowned!"
They called aloud, "Our sieve ain't big;
But we don't care a button, we don't care a fig:
   In a sieve we'll go to sea!"
     Far and few, far and few,
       Are the lands where the Jumblies live:
       Their heads are green, and their hands are blue;
       And they went to sea in a sieve.

They sailed away in a sieve, they did,
   In a sieve they sailed so fast,
With only a beautiful pea-green veil
Tied with a ribbon, by way of a sail,
   To a small tobacco-pipe mast.
And every one said who saw them go,
"Oh! won't they be soon upset, you know?
For the sky is dark, and the voyage is long;
And, happen what may, it's extremely wrong
   In a sieve to sail so fast."
     Far and few, far and few,
       Are the lands where the Jumblies live:
       Their heads are green, and their hands are blue;
       And they went to sea in a sieve.

The water it soon came in, it did;
  The water it soon came in:
So, to keep them dry, they wrapped their feet
In a pinky paper all folded neat;
  And they fastened it down with a pin.
And they passed the night in a crockery-jar;
And each of them said, "How wise we are!
Though the sky be dark, and the voyage be long,
Yet we never can think we were rash or wrong,
  While round in our sieve we spin."
    Far and few, far and few,
      Are the lands where the Jumblies live:
      Their heads are green, and their hands are blue;
      And they went to sea in a sieve.

And all night long they sailed away;
  And when the sun went down,
They whistled and warbled a moony song,
To the echoing sound of a coppery gong,
  In the shade of the mountains brown.
"O Timballoo! How happy we are
When we live in a sieve and a crockery-jar!
And all night long, in the moonlight pale,
We sail away with a pea-green sail
  In the shade of the mountains brown."
    Far and few, far and few,
      Are the lands where the Jumblies live:
      Their heads are green, and their hands are blue;
      And they went to sea in a sieve.

They sailed to the Western Sea, they did,—
　To a land all covered with trees:
And they bought an owl, and a useful cart,
And a pound of rice, and a cranberry-tart,
　And a hive of silvery bees;
And they bought a pig, and some green jackdaws,
And a lovely monkey with lollipop paws,
And forty bottles of ring-bo-ree,
　And no end of Stilton cheese.
　　Far and few, far and few,
　　　Are the lands where the Jumblies live:
　　Their heads are green, and their hands are blue;
　　　And they went to sea in a sieve.

And in twenty years they all came back,—
　In twenty years or more;
And every one said, "How tall they've grown!
For they've been to the Lakes, and the Torrible Zone,
　And the hills of the Chankly Bore."
And they drank their health, and gave them a feast
Of dumplings made of beautiful yeast;
And every one said, "If we only live,
We, too, will go to sea in a sieve,
　To the hills of the Chankly Bore."
　　Far and few, far and few,
　　　Are the lands where the Jumblies live:
　　Their heads are green, and their hands are blue;
　　　And they went to sea in a sieve.

Edward Lear

MAGIC
AND
MAKE BELIEVE

I cannot see fairies.
I dream them.

FAIRIES

I cannot see fairies.
I dream them.
There is no fairy can hide from me;
I keep on dreaming till I find him:
There you are, Primrose! I see you, Black Wing!

Hilda Conkling, *Poems by a Little Girl*
Copyright 1920 by J. B. Lippincott Company

HAVE YOU WATCHED THE FAIRIES?

Have you watched the fairies when the rain is done
Spreading out their little wings to dry them in the sun?
  I have, I have! Isn't it fun?

Have you heard the fairies all among the limes
Singing little fairy tunes to little fairy rhymes?
  I have, I have, lots and lots of times!

Have you seen the fairies dancing in the air,
And dashing off behind the stars to tidy up their hair?
  I have, I have; I've been there!

Rose Fyleman, *Fairies and Chimneys*
Copyright 1920 by Doubleday & Company, Inc., New York
Copyright 1948 by Rose Fyleman
By permission of The Society of Authors, *Punch,*
and Messrs. Methuen & Co., Ltd., London

COULD

IT HAVE BEEN

A SHADOW?

What ran under the rosebush?
  What ran under the stone?
Could it have been a shadow,
  Running away alone?
Maybe a fairy's shadow,
  Slipping away at dawn
To guard a gleaming pot of gold
  For a busy leprechaun.

Monica Shannon, *Goose Grass Rhymes*
Copyright 1930 by Doubleday & Company, Inc.

YESTERDAY

IN

OXFORD

STREET

Yesterday in Oxford Street, oh, what d'you think, my dears?
I had the most exciting time I've had for years and years;
The buildings looked so straight and tall, the sky was blue between,
And, riding on a motor-bus, I saw the fairy queen!

Sitting there upon the rail and bobbing up and down,
The sun was shining on her wings and on her golden crown;
And looking at the shops she was, the pretty silks and lace—
She seemed to think that Oxford Street was quite a lovely place.

And once she turned and looked at me, and waved her little hand;
But I could only stare and stare—oh, would she understand?
I simply couldn't speak at all, I simply couldn't stir,
And all the rest of Oxford Street was just a shining blur.

Then suddenly she shook her wings—a bird had fluttered by—
And down into the street she looked and up into the sky;
And perching on the railing on a tiny fairy toe,
She flashed away so quickly that I hardly saw her go.

I never saw her any more, altho' I looked all day;
Perhaps she only came to peep, and never meant to stay:
But oh, my dears, just think of it, just think what luck for me,
That she should come to Oxford Street, and I be there to see!

Rose Fyleman, *Fairies and Chimneys*

WHEN A RING'S AROUND THE MOON

The wee folk will be tripping,
  In their silver dancing shoon,
Ring-around-the-meadow,
  When a ring's around the moon:

Curtsy to the right and left,
  And curtsy to the middle—
The fiddler will be fiddling
  On his tiny fairy fiddle;

In and out and round about,
  A magic circle making;
The pipers will be piping
  Till their tiny throats are aching.

Oh, few may watch the wee ones dance,
  For fairy guards are spying,
And down beneath the grasses
  All the dancers will be hieing;

But hearken well, what time you see
  A ring around the moon;
And you will hear the music
  Of the wee folks' dancing tune.

Mary Jane Carr, *Top of the Morning*

CRAB-APPLE

I dreamed the Fairies wanted me
   To spend my birth-night with them all;
And I said, "Oh, but you're so wee
   And I am so tremendous tall,
What could we do?"
   "Crab-apple stem!"
Said they, and I was just like them.

And then, when we were all the same,
   The party and the fun began;
They said they'd teach me a new game
   Of "Dew-ponds." "I don't think I can
Play that," I said.
   "Crab-apple blue!"
Said they, and I could play it too.

And then, when we had played and played,
   The Fairies said that we would dance;
And I said, "Oh, but I'm afraid
   That I've no shoes." I gave a glance
At my bare toes.
   "Crab-apple sweet!"
Said they, and shoes were on my feet.

And then we danced away, away,
   Until my birth-night all was done;
And I said, "I'll go home to-day;
   And thank you for my lovely fun,
I'll come again."
   "Crab-apple red!"
Said they, and I woke up in bed.

Ethel Talbot
Reproduced by permission of the Proprietors of *Punch*

MIDSUMMER

MAGIC

Midsummer Eve, a year ago, my mother she commanded,
"Now don't you go a'running down to Ragwort Meadow!
And don't you go a'plucking of the bracken-seed or nightshade;
Stay out of the moonlight, mind! and keep out of the shadow,
   For they say that the Ragtag,
               Bobtail,
               Merry-derry
               Fairy-men
Tonight will go a'dancing down in Ragwort Meadow!"

Midsummer Eve, a year ago, my mother she commanded,
"Now don't you go a'playing down in Ragwort Meadow!
Keep away from thorn-tree, from adders' tongue and henbane!
Keep away from moonlight and don't venture in the shadow,
   For they say that the Ragtag,
               Bobtail,
               Merry-derry
               Fairy-men
Are out a'snaring mortals down in Ragwort Meadow."

I wouldn't heed my mother's words! I wouldn't heed her warning!
I ran through the moonlight, through the starlight and the shadow!
And I never stopped a'running though my breath came quick and
    gasping,

Till I reached the very middle of Ragwort Meadow,
    And there I heard the Ragtag,
                    Bobtail,
                    Merry-derry
                    Fairy-men
A'laughing fit to kill themselves in Ragwort Meadow.

I heard 'em! But I couldn't see, no! not a little sight of 'em!
I pulled a curly bracken-leaf a'growing in the meadow,
I scratched out all the bracken-seeds and rubbed them on my eyelids—
The moon gave brilliant sunlight! There wasn't any shadow!
    And there I saw the Ragtag,
                    Bobtail,
                    Merry-derry
                    Fairy-men
A'dancing round me in a ring in Ragwort Meadow.

Half-a-hundred fairy-men and half-a-score of rabbits;
Half-a-dozen squirrels down in Ragwort Meadow,
Dancing round me in a ring—you never saw the like of it!—
Underneath the daylight which the bright moon shed! Oh!
    A blessing on the Ragtag,
                    Bobtail,
                    Merry-derry
                    Fairy-men
Who showed themselves to me down in Ragwort Meadow.

Ivy O. Eastwick, *Fairies and Suchlike*
Published and copyright 1946 by E. P. Dutton & Co., Inc., New York

333

STOCKING
FAIRY

In a hole of the heel of an old brown stocking,
A little old Fairy sits rocking and rocking,
And scolding and pointing and squeaking and squinting,
Brown as a nut, a bright eye glinting,
She tugs at a thread, she drags up a needle,
She stamps and she shrills, she commences to wheedle,
To whine of the cold, in a fine gust of temper
She beats on my thumb, and then with a whimper
She sulks in her shawl, she says I've forgotten
I promised to make her a lattice of cotton,
A soft, woven window, cozy yet airy,
Where she could sit rocking and peeking—Hush, Fairy,
Tush, Fairy, sit gently, look sweetly,
I'll do what I said, now, and close you in neatly.

Winifred Welles, *Skipping Along Alone*
The Macmillan Company, New York, 1931

THE

PLUMPUPPETS

When little heads weary have gone to their bed,
When all the good nights and the prayers have been said,
Of all the good fairies that send bairns to rest
The little Plumpuppets are those I love best.

If your pillow is lumpy, or hot, thin and flat,
The little Plumpuppets know just what they're at;
They plump up the pillow, all soft, cool and fat—
The little Plumpuppets plump-up it!

The little Plumpuppets are fairies of beds:
They have nothing to do but to watch sleepy heads;
They turn down the sheets and they tuck you in tight,
And they dance on your pillow to wish you good night!

No matter what troubles have bothered the day,
Though your doll broke her arm or the pup ran away;
Though your handies are black with the ink that was spilt—
Plumpuppets are waiting in blanket and quilt.

If your pillow is lumpy, or hot, thin and flat,
The little Plumpuppets know just what they're at;
They plump up the pillow, all soft, cool and fat—
The little Plumpuppets plump-up it!

Christopher Morley, *The Rocking Horse*
Copyright 1918, 1946 by Christopher Morley
Published by J. B. Lippincott Company

THE
ROCK-A-BY
LADY

The Rock-a-By Lady from Hushaby street
   Comes stealing; comes creeping;
The poppies they hang from her head to her feet,
And each hath a dream that is tiny and fleet—
She bringeth her poppies to you, my sweet,
   When she findeth you sleeping!

There is one little dream of a beautiful drum—
   "Rub-a-dub!" it goeth;
There is one little dream of a big sugar-plum,
And lo! thick and fast the other dreams come
Of popguns that bang, and tin tops that hum,
   And a trumpet that bloweth!

And dollies peep out of those wee little dreams
   With laughter and singing;
And boats go a-floating on silvery streams,
And the stars peek-a-boo with their own misty gleams,
And up, up, and up, where the Mother Moon beams,
   The fairies go winging!

Would you dream all these dreams that are tiny and fleet?
   They'll come to you sleeping;
So shut the two eyes that are weary, my sweet,
For the Rock-a-By Lady from Hushaby street,
With poppies that hang from her head to her feet,
   Comes stealing; comes creeping.

Eugene Field, *Poems of Childhood*
Charles Scribner's Sons, New York, 1904

TIGGADY RUE

Curious, curious Tiggady Rue
Looks and looks in the heart of you;
She finds you good,
She finds you bad,
Generous, mean,
Grumpy, glad—
Tiggady Rue.

Curious, curious Tiggady Rue
Tells your thoughts and tells you *you;*
Elephant thoughts,
And spry and lean,
And thoughts made like a jumping bean,
Or wedgy ones
Slid in between—
She knows them, too,
If she looks at you,
Tiggady Rue.

Curious, curious Tiggady Rue
Knows your thoughts and you and you.
When dusk is down
On field and town,
Beware!
Take care!
If she looks at you—
Tiggady Rue.

David McCord, *Far and Few*
Copyright 1929, 1931, 1952 by David McCord
By permission of Little, Brown & Company, Boston

THE GOBLIN   (*French*)

A goblin lives in *our* house, in *our* house, in *our* house,
A goblin lives in *our* house all the year round.
He bumps
And he jumps
And he thumps
And he stumps.
He knocks
And he rocks
And he rattles at the locks.
A goblin lives in *our* house, in *our* house, in *our* house,
A goblin lives in *our* house all the year round.

Rose Fyleman, *Picture Rhymes from Foreign Lands*
Copyright 1935 by Rose Fyleman
Reprinted by permission of J. B. Lippincott Company

LITTLE ORPHANT ANNIE

Little Orphant Annie's come to our house to stay,
An' wash the cups an' saucers up, an' brush the crumbs away,
An' shoo the chickens off the porch, an' dust the hearth, an' sweep,
An' make the fire, an' bake the bread, an' earn her board-an'-keep;
An' all us other children, when the supper things is done,
We set around the kitchen fire an' has the mostest fun
A-list'nin' to the witch-tales 'at Annie tells about,
An' the Gobble-uns 'at gits you
                    Ef you
                 Don't
                 Watch
                 Out!

Onc't they was a little boy wouldn't say his prayers,
An' when he went to bed at night, away upstairs,
His Mammy heerd him holler, an' his Daddy heerd him bawl,
An' when they turn't the kivvers down, he wasn't there at all!

338

An' they seeked him in the rafter room, an' cubby-hole, an' press,
An' seeked him up the chimbly-flue, an' ever'wheres, I guess;
But all they ever found was thist his pants an' roundabout:—
An' the Gobble-uns 'll git you
                    Ef you
                  Don't
                  Watch
                  Out!

An' one time a little girl 'ud allus laugh an' grin,
An' make fun of ever'one, an' all her blood an' kin;
An' onc't, when they was "company," an' ole folks was there,
She mocked 'em an' shocked 'em, an' said she didn't care!
An' thist as she kicked her heels, an' turn't to run an' hide,
They was two great big Black Things a-standin' by her side,
An' they snatched her through the ceilin' 'fore she knowed what she's
    about!
An' the Gobble-uns 'll git you
                    Ef you
                  Don't
                  Watch
                  Out!

An' little Orphant Annie says, when the blaze is blue,
An' the lamp-wick sputters, an' the wind goes *woo-oo!*
An' you hear the crickets quit, an' the moon is gray,
An' the lightnin'-bugs in dew is all squenched away,—
You better mind yer parents, an' yer teachers fond an' dear,
An' churish them 'at loves you, an' dry the orphant's tear,
An' he'p the pore an' needy ones 'at clusters all about,
Er the Gobble-uns 'll git you
                    Ef you
                  Don't
                  Watch
                  Out!

James Whitcomb Riley

339

A GOBLINADE

A green hobgoblin,
  Small but quick,
Went out walking
  With a black thorn stick.

He was full of mischief,
  Full of glee.
He frightened all
  That he could see.

He saw a little maiden
  In a wood.
He looked as fierce as
  A goblin should.

He crept by the hedge row,
  He said, "Boo!"
"Boo!" laughed the little girl,
  "How are you?"

"What!" said the goblin,
  "Aren't you afraid?"
"I think you're funny,"
  Said the maid.

"Ha!" said the goblin,
  Sitting down flat.
"You think I'm funny?
  I don't like that.

"I'm very frightening.
  You should flee!"
"You're cunning," she said,
  "As you can be!"

Then she laughed again, and
  Went away.
But the goblin stood there
  All that day.

A beetle came by, and
  "Well?" it said.
But the goblin only
  Shook his head.

"For I am funny,"
  He said to it.
"I thought I was alarming,
  And I'm not a bit.

"If I'm amusing,"
  He said to himself,
"I won't be a goblin,
  I'll be an elf!

"For a goblin must be goblin
  All the day,
But an elf need only
  Dance and play."

So the little green goblin
  Became an elf.
And he dances all day, and
  He likes himself.

In *Child Life*, October 1927
Copyright 1927 by Rand McNally & Company
By permission of the author

OVERHEARD ON A SALTMARSH

Nymph, nymph, what are your beads?

Green glass, goblin. Why do you stare at them?

Give them me.

          No.

Give them me. Give them me.

              No.

Then I will howl all night in the reeds,
Lie in the mud and howl for them.

Goblin, why do you love them so?

They are better than stars or water,
Better than voices of winds that sing,
Better than any man's fair daughter,
Your green glass beads on a silver ring.

Hush, I stole them out of the moon.

Give me your beads, I desire them.

              No.

I will howl in a deep lagoon
For your green glass beads, I love them so.
Give them me. Give them.

          No.

Harold Monro, *Children of Love*
The Poetry Bookshop, London, 1913

HOW TO TELL GOBLINS FROM ELVES

The Goblin has a wider mouth
　　Than any wondering elf.
The saddest part of this is that
　　He brings it on himself.
For hanging in a willow clump
　　In baskets made of sheaves,
You may see the baby goblins
　　Under coverlets of leaves.

They suck a pink and podgy foot,
　　(As human babies do),
And then they suck the other one,
　　Until they're sucking two.
And so it is that goblins' mouths
　　Keep growing very round.
So you can't mistake a goblin,
　　When a goblin you have found.

Monica Shannon, *Goose Grass Rhymes*
Copyright 1930 by Doubleday & Company, Inc.

THE LITTLE ELFMAN

I met a little Elfman once,
　　Down where the lilies blow.
I asked him why he was so small,
　　And why he didn't grow.

He slightly frowned, and with his eye
　　He looked me through and through—
"I'm just as big for me," said he,
　　"As you are big for you!"

John Kendrick Bangs
In *St. Nicholas*, 1893

THE ELF AND THE DORMOUSE

Under a toadstool
  Crept a wee Elf,
Out of the rain
  To shelter himself.

Under the toadstool,
  Sound asleep,
Sat a big Dormouse
  All in a heap.

Trembled the wee Elf,
  Frightened, and yet
Fearing to fly away
  Lest he get wet.

To the next shelter—
  Maybe a mile!
Sudden the wee Elf
  Smiled a wee smile,

Tugged till the toadstool
  Toppled in two.
Holding it over him
  Gaily he flew.

Soon he was safe home
  Dry as could be.
Soon woke the Dormouse—
  "Good gracious me!

Where is my toadstool?"
  Loud he lamented.
—And that's how umbrellas,
  First were invented.

Oliver Herford, *Artful Anticks*
The Century Company, New York, 1901

344

THE MAN WHO HID HIS OWN FRONT DOOR

There was a little, Elvish man
  Who lived beside a moor,
A shy, secretive, furtive soul
  Who hid his own front door.

He went and hid his door beneath
  A pink laburnum bush:
The neighbors saw the curtains blow,
  They heard a singing thrush.

The Banker came and jingled gold,
  It did not serve him there;
The honey-colored walls uprose
  Unbroken and foresquare.

The Mayor called, the Misses Pitt
  With cordials and game pie;
There was not any door at all,
  They had to pass him by!

But ah! my little sister.
  Her eyes were wild and sweet,
She wore blue faded calico,
  And no shoes on her feet.

She found the wandering door in place
  And easily went through
Into a strange and mossy Hall
  Where bowls of old Delft blue

Held feasts of blackberries, like gems
  In webs of shining dew—
There stood that little Elvish man
  And smiled to see her, too!

Elizabeth MacKinstry
In *Gaily We Parade*
The Macmillan Company, New York, 1940

345

Where the bee sucks, there suck I:
In a cowslip's bell I lie;
There I couch when owls do cry.
On the bat's back I do fly
After summer merrily.
Merrily, merrily, shall I live now
Under the blossom that hangs on the bough.

William Shakespeare

THE

GNOME

I saw a gnome
As plain as plain
Sitting on top
Of a weathervane.

He was dressed like a crow
In silky black feathers,
And there he sat watching
All kinds of weathers.

He talked like a crow too,
Caw caw caw,
When he told me exactly
What he saw,

Snow to the north of him
Sun to the south,
And he spoke with a beaky
Kind of a mouth.

But he wasn't a crow,
That was plain as plain
'Cause crows never sit
On a weathervane.

What I saw was simply
A usual gnome
Looking things over
On his way home.

Harry Behn, *Windy Morning*
Copyright 1953 by Harry Behn
By permission of Harcourt, Brace and Company, Inc., New York

SOME

ONE

Some one came knocking
  At my wee, small door;
Some one came knocking,
  I'm sure—sure—sure;
I listened, I opened,
  I looked to left and right,
But nought there was a-stirring
  In the still dark night;
Only the busy beetle
  Tap-tapping in the wall,
Only from the forest
  The screech-owl's call,
Only the cricket whistling
  While the dewdrops fall,
So I know not who came knocking,
  At all, at all, at all.

Walter de la Mare, *Collected Poems, 1901–1918*
Copyright 1920 by Henry Holt and Company, Inc.
Copyright 1948 by Walter de la Mare
Reprinted by permission of the publishers
(Also in *Rhymes and Verses* by Walter de la Mare
Published by Henry Holt and Company, Inc., New York, 1947)

SLEEPYHEAD

As I lay awake in the white moonlight,
I heard a faint singing in the wood,
  "Out of bed,
  Sleepyhead,
  Put your white foot now,
  Here are we,
  Neath the tree
  Singing round the root now!"

I looked out of window, in the white moonlight,
The trees were like snow in the wood—
  "Come away,
  Child, and play
  Light with the gnomies;
  In a mound,
  Green and round,
  That's where their home is.

  "Honey sweet,
  Curds to eat,
  Cream and fruménty,
  Shells and beads,
  Poppy seeds,
  You shall have plenty."

But soon as I stooped in the dim moonlight
To put on my stocking and my shoe,
The sweet, sweet singing died sadly away,
And the light of the morning peeped through:
Then instead of the gnomies there came a red robin
To sing of the buttercups and dew.

Walter de la Mare, *Collected Poems, 1901–1918*

Copyright 1920 by Henry Holt and Company, Inc.
Copyright 1948 by Walter de la Mare
Reprinted by permission of the publishers
(Also in *Rhymes and Verses* by Walter de la Mare
Published by Henry Holt and Company, Inc., New York, 1947)

FOR A MOCKING VOICE

Who   calls?   Who   calls?   Who?
Did you call?   Did you?—
I call!   I call!   I!
Follow where I fly.—
Where?   O where?   O where?
On Earth or in the Air?—
Where you come, I'm gone!
Where you fly, I've flown!—
Stay! ah, stay! ah, stay,
Pretty Elf, and play!
Tell me where you are—
Ha, ha, ha, ha, ha!

Eleanor Farjeon, *Collection of Poems*
Copyright 1929, 1957 by Eleanor Farjeon
Published by J. B. Lippincott Company, Philadelphia

THE BAGPIPE MAN

The bagpipe man came over our hill
    When no one knew he was anywhere round,
With a whirl and a skirl, a toot and a trill;
    And we all went scampering after the sound.
We cried, "Oh, tell us, what do you play?
    What do you play so queer, so queer?"
And he skipped a couple of notes to say,
    "But tell me, what do ye hear?"

Then one of us heard a trumpet sweet,
    And the tramp, tramp, tramp of marching men;
And one of us heard the dancing feet
    Of fairies down in a dusky glen;
And one of us called it a bird in June,
    And one, a river that ran and ran.
But he never would tell us the name of his tune,
    The funny old bagpipe man!

Nancy Byrd Turner, *Magpie Lane*
Copyright 1927 by Harcourt, Brace and Company, Inc., New York
Copyright 1956 by Nancy Byrd Turner

349

THE FIDDLER OF DOONEY

When I play on my fiddle in Dooney,
Folk dance like a wave of the sea;
My cousin is priest in Kilvarnet,
My brother in Moharabuiee.

I passed my brother and cousin:
They read in their books of prayer;
I read in my book of songs
I bought at the Sligo fair.

When we come at the end of time
To Peter sitting in state,
He will smile on the three old spirits,
But call me first through the gate;

For the good are always the merry,
Save by an evil chance,
And the merry love the fiddle
And the merry love to dance:

And when the folk there spy me,
They will all come up to me,
With "Here is the fiddler of Dooney!"
And dance like a wave of the sea.

William Butler Yeats, *Poetical Works*

Copyright 1906, 1934 by The Macmillan Company
and used with their permission
By permission also of Mrs. William Butler Yeats

TILLIE

Old Tillie Turveycombe
Sat to sew,
Just where a patch of fern did grow;
There, as she yawned,
And yawn wide did she,
Floated some seed
Down her gull-e-t;
And look you once,
And look you twice,
Poor old Tillie
Was gone in a trice.
But oh, when the wind
Do a-moaning come,
'Tis poor old Tillie
Sick for home;
And oh, when a voice
In the mist do sigh,
Old Tillie Turveycombe's
Floating by.

Walter de la Mare, *Collected Poems, 1901–1918*

Copyright 1920 by Henry Holt and Company, Inc.
Copyright 1948 by Walter de la Mare
Reprinted by permission of the publishers
(Also in *Rhymes and Verses* by Walter de la Mare
Published by Henry Holt and Company, Inc., New York, 1947)

BERRIES

There was an old woman
   Went blackberry picking
Along the hedges
   From Weep to Wicking.
Half a pottle—
   No more she had got,
When out steps a Fairy
   From her green grot;

And says, "Well, Jill,
  Would 'ee pick 'ee mo?"
And Jill, she curtseys,
  And looks just so.
"Be off," says the Fairy,
  "As quick as you can,
Over the meadows
  To the little green lane,
That dips to the hayfields
  Of Farmer Grimes:
I've berried those hedges
  A score of times;
Bushel on bushel
  I'll promise 'ee, Jill,
This side of supper
  If 'ee pick with a will."
She glints very bright,
  And speaks her fair;
Then lo, and behold!
  She had faded in air.

Be sure Old Goodie
  She trots betimes
Over the meadows
  To Farmer Grimes.
And never was queen
  With jewellery rich
As those same hedges
  From twig to ditch;
Like Dutchmen's coffers,
  Fruit, thorn, and flower—
They shone like William
  And Mary's bower.
And be sure Old Goodie
  Went back to Weep

So tired with her basket
  She scarce could creep.

When she comes in the dusk
  To her cottage door,
There's Towser wagging
  As never before,
To see his Missus
  So glad to be
Come from her fruit-picking
  Back to he.
As soon as next morning
  Dawn was grey,
The pot on the hob
  Was simmering away;
And all in a stew
  And a hugger-mugger
Towser and Jill
  A-boiling of sugar,
And the dark clear fruit
  That from Faërie came,
For syrup and jelly
  And blackberry jam.

Twelve jolly gallipots
  Jill put by;
And one little teeny one,
  One inch high;
And that she's hidden
  A good thumb deep,
Halfway over
  From Wicking to Weep.

Walter de la Mare, *Collected Poems, 1901–1918*

Copyright 1920 by Henry Holt and Company, Inc.
Copyright 1948 by Walter de la Mare
Reprinted by permission of the publishers
(Also in *Rhymes and Verses* by Walter de la Mare
Published by Henry Holt and Company, Inc., New York, 1947)

BEHIND THE WATERFALL

A little old woman
  In a thin white shawl,
Stepped straight through the column
  Of the silver waterfall,
As if the fall of water
  Were not anything at all.
I saw her crook her finger,
  I heard her sweetly call.
Over stones all green and glossy
  I fled and did not fall;
I ran along the river
  And through the waterfall,
And that heavy curve of water
  Never hindered me at all.
The little old woman
  In the thin white shawl
Took my hand and laughed and led me
  Down a cool, still hall,
Between two rows of pillars
  That were glistening and tall.
At her finger's tap swung open
  A wide door in the wall,
And I saw the crystal city
  That's behind the waterfall.

Winifred Welles, *Skipping Along Alone*
The Macmillan Company, New York, 1931

SAM

When Sam goes back in memory,
  It is to where the sea
Breaks on the shingle, emerald-green
  In white foam, endlessly;
He says—with small brown eye on mine—
  "I used to keep awake,

354

And lean from my window in the moon,
   Watching those billows break.
And half a million tiny hands,
   And eyes, like sparks of frost,
Would dance and come tumbling into the moon,
   On every breaker tossed.
And all across from star to star,
   I've seen the watery sea,
With not a single ship in sight,
   Just ocean there, and me;
And heard my father snore . . . And once,
   As sure as I'm alive,
Out of those wallowing, moon-flecked waves
   I saw a mermaid dive;
Head and shoulders above the wave,
   Plain as I now see you,
Combing her hair, now back, now front,
   Her two eyes peeping through;
Calling me, 'Sam!'—quietlike—'Sam!' . . .
   But me . . . I never went,
Making believe I kind of thought
   'Twas someone else she meant . . .
Wonderful lovely there she sat,
   Singing the night away,
All in the solitudinous sea
   Of that there lonely bay.
P'raps," and he'd smooth his hairless mouth,
   "P'raps, if 'twere *now*, my son,
P'raps, if I heard a voice say, 'Sam!' . . .
   Morning would find me gone."

Walter de la Mare, *Collected Poems, 1901–1918*

Copyright 1920 by Henry Holt and Company, Inc.
Copyright 1948 by Walter de la Mare
Reprinted by permission of the publishers
(Also in *Rhymes and Verses* by Walter de la Mare
Published by Henry Holt and Company, Inc., New York, 1947)

THE HORSEMAN

I heard a horseman
　Ride over the hill;
The moon shone clear,
　The night was still;
His helm was silver,
　And pale was he;
And the horse he rode
　Was of ivory.

Walter de la Mare, *Rhymes and Verses*
Published by Henry Holt & Company, Inc., New York, 1947
By permission of the literary trustees of Walter de la Mare
and The Society of Authors, London, as their representatives

THE UNICORN

While yet the Morning Star
Flamed in the sky
A Unicorn went mincing by,
Whiter by far than blossom of the thorn:
His silver horn
Glittered as he danced and pranced
Silver-pale in the silver-pale morn.

The folk that saw him, ran away.

Where he went, so gay, so fleet,
Star-like lilies at his feet
Flowered all day,
Lilies, lilies in a throng,
And the wind made for him a song:

But he dared not stay
Over-long!

Ella Young
In *The Horn Book*, March–April 1939
By permission of The Horn Book Inc., Boston

FAITH, I WISH I WERE A LEPRECHAUN

Faith, I wish I were a leprechaun
Beneath a hawthorn tree,
A-cobblin' of wee, magic boots,
A-eatin' luscious, lovely fruits;
Oh, fiddle-dum, oh, fiddle-dee,
I wish I were a leprechaun
Beneath a hawthorn tree!

Faith, I wish I were a leprechaun
Beneath a hawthorn tree,
A-throwin' snuff into the eyes
Of young and old and dull and wise;
Oh, fiddle-dum, oh, fiddle-dee,
I wish I were a leprechaun
Beneath a hawthorn tree!

Faith, I wish I were a leprechaun
Beneath a hawthorn tree,
With no more irksome thing to do
Than sew a small, bewitchin' shoe;
Oh, fiddle-dum, oh, fiddle-dee,
I wish I were a leprechaun
Beneath a hawthorn tree!

Margaret Ritter, *Mirrors*

INTRODUCTION TO SONGS OF INNOCENCE

Piping down the valleys wild,
    Piping songs of pleasant glee,
On a cloud I saw a child,
    And he laughing said to me:

"Pipe a song about a Lamb!"
    So I piped with merry cheer.
"Piper, pipe that song again";
    So I piped; he wept to hear.

"Drop thy pipe, thy happy pipe;
    Sing thy songs of happy cheer!"
So I sang the same again,
    While he wept with joy to hear.

"Piper, sit thee down and write
    In a book, that all may read."
So he vanished from my sight;
    And I plucked a hollow reed,

And I made a rural pen,
    And I stained the water clear,
And I wrote my happy songs
    Every child may joy to hear.

William Blake

THE SONG OF WANDERING AENGUS

I went out to the hazel wood,
Because a fire was in my head,
And cut and peeled a hazel wand,
And hooked a berry to a thread;
And when white moths were on the wing,
And moth-like stars were flickering out,
I dropped a berry in a stream
And caught a little silver trout.

When I had laid it on the floor
I went to blow the fire aflame,
But something rustled on the floor,
And some one called me by my name:
It had become a glimmering girl
With apple blossom in her hair
Who called me by my name and ran
And faded through the brightening air.

Though I am old with wandering
Through hollow lands and hilly lands,
I will find out where she has gone,
And kiss her lips and take her hands;
And walk among long dappled grass,
And pluck till time and times are done
The silver apples of the moon,
The golden apples of the sun.

William Butler Yeats, *Poetical Works*
Copyright 1906, 1934 by The Macmillan Company
and used with their permission
By permission also of Mrs. William Butler Yeats

KIPH

My Uncle Ben, who's been
To Bisk, Bhir, Biak—
Been, and come back:
To Tab, Tau, Tze, and Tomsk,
And home, by Teneriffe:
Who, brown as desert sand,
Gaunt, staring, slow and stiff,
Has chased the Unicorn
And Hippogriff,
Gave me a smooth, small, shining stone,
Called *Kiph.*

"Look'ee, now, Nevvy mine,"
He told me—"*If*
You'd wish a wish,
Just rub this smooth, small, shining stone,
Called *Kiph.*"

Hide it did I,
In a safe, secret spot;
Slept, and the place
In dreams forgot.

One wish *alone*
Now's mine: Oh, if
I could but find again
That stone called *Kiph!*

Walter de la Mare, *Rhymes and Verses*

Published by Henry Holt & Company, Inc., New York, 1947
By permission of the literary trustees of Walter de la Mare
and The Society of Authors, London, as their representatives

WIND
AND
WATER

Weather is the answer
When I can't go out into flowery places.

WEATHER

Weather is the answer
When I can't go out into flowery places;
Weather is my wonder
About the kind of morning
Hidden behind the hills of sky.

WATER

The world turns softly
Not to spill its lakes and rivers.
The water is held in its arms
And the sky is held in the water.
What is water,
That pours silver,
And can hold the sky?

Little wind, blow on the hill-top,
Little wind, blow down the plain;
Little wind, blow up the sunshine,
Little wind, blow off the rain.

Blow wind, blow, and go mill, go,
That the miller may grind his corn;
That the baker may take it,
And into bread bake it,
And bring us a loaf in the morn.

Mother Goose

WINDY

WASH DAY

The wash is hanging on the line
And the wind's blowing—
Dresses all so clean and fine,
Beckoning
And bowing.

Stockings twisting in a dance,
Pajamas very tripping,
And every little pair of pants
Upside down
And skipping.

Dorothy Aldis, *Hop, Skip and Jump*
Minton, Balch and Company, New York, 1934
Copyright 1934 by Dorothy Aldis

A KITE

I often sit and wish that I
Could be a kite up in the sky,
And ride upon the breeze and go
Whichever way I chanced to blow.

Unknown

THE KITE

How bright on the blue
Is a kite when it's new!

With a dive and a dip
It snaps its tail

Then soars like a ship
With only a sail

As over tides
Of wind it rides,

Climbs to the crest
Of a gust and pulls,

Then seems to rest
As wind falls.

When string goes slack
You wind it back

And run until
A new breeze blows

And its wings fill
And up it goes!

How bright on the blue
Is a kite when it's new!

But a raggeder thing
You never will see

When it flaps on a string
In the top of a tree.

Harry Behn, *Windy Morning*
Copyright 1953 by Harry Behn
By permission of Harcourt, Brace and Company, Inc., New York

THE WIND

I saw you toss the kites on high
And blow the birds about the sky;
And all around I heard you pass,
Like ladies' skirts across the grass—
    O wind, a-blowing all day long,
    O wind, that sings so loud a song!

I saw the different things you did,
But always you yourself you hid.
I felt you push, I heard you call,
I could not see yourself at all—
    O wind, a-blowing all day long,
    O wind, that sings so loud a song!

O you that are so strong and cold,
O blower, are you young or old?
Are you a beast of field and tree,
Or just a stronger child than me?
    O wind, a-blowing all day long,
    O wind, that sings so loud a song!

Robert Louis Stevenson, *A Child's Garden of Verses*

Who has seen the wind?
    Neither I nor you:
But when the leaves hang trembling
    The wind is passing thro'.

Who has seen the wind?
    Neither you nor I:
But when the trees bow down their heads
    The wind is passing by.

Christina Georgina Rossetti, *Sing-Song*

WINDY

NIGHTS

Whenever the moon and stars are set,
  Whenever the wind is high,
All night long in the dark and wet,
  A man goes riding by.
Late in the night when the fires are out,
Why does he gallop and gallop about?

Whenever the trees are crying aloud,
  And ships are tossed at sea,
By, on the highway, low and loud,
  By at the gallop goes he:
By at the gallop he goes, and then
By he comes back at the gallop again.

Robert Louis Stevenson, *A Child's Garden of Verses*

The wind has such a rainy sound
  Moaning through the town,
The sea has such a windy sound,—
  Will the ships go down?

The apples in the orchard
  Tumble from their tree.—
Oh, will the ships go down, go down,
  In the windy sea?

Christina Georgina Rossetti, *Sing-Song*

THE NOISE OF WATERS

All day I hear the noise of waters
  Making moan,
Sad as the sea-bird is, when going
  Forth alone,
He hears the winds cry to the waters'
  Monotone.

The grey winds, the cold winds are blowing
  Where I go.
I hear the noise of many waters
  Far below.
All day, all night, I hear them flowing
  To and fro.

James Joyce, *Collected Poems*

WIND-WOLVES

Do you hear the cry as the pack goes by,
The wind-wolves hunting across the sky?
Hear them tongue it, keen and clear,
Hot on the flanks of the flying deer!

Across the forest, mere, and plain,
Their hunting howl goes up again!
All night they'll follow the ghostly trail,
All night we'll hear their phantom wail,

For tonight the wind-wolf pack holds sway
From Pegasus Square to the Milky Way,
And the frightened bands of cloud-deer flee
In scattered groups of two and three.

William D. Sargent

STORM

You crash over the trees,
you crack the live branch—
the branch is white,
the green crushed,
each leaf is rent like split wood.

You burden the trees
with black drops,
you swirl and crash—
you have broken off a weighted leaf
in the wind,
it is hurled out,
whirls up and sinks,
a green stone.

Hilda Doolittle Aldington, *Sea Garden*
Jonathan Cape Limited, London, 1924

O wind, why do you never rest,
    Wandering, whistling to and fro,
Bringing rain out of the west,
    From the dim north bringing snow?

Christina Georgina Rossetti, *Sing-Song*

White sheep, white sheep,
On a blue hill,
When the wind stops
You all stand still.
When the wind blows
You walk away slow.
White sheep, white sheep,
Where do you go?

Unknown

SUMMER SKY

I like the clouds.
I never knew
So many things went sailing through
The sky.
I like the clouds
Because they make
Things like white boats on a lake,
And high,
High mountains
Far away.
I could sit and watch all day . . .
While sheep
Asleep,
And men,
And sheep again,
And trees,
And bees,
And birds,
And herds
Of cows
Go by.
I like the clouds up in the sky.

Ruth McKee Gordon

In *Poems to Grow On*
Copyright © 1957 by Jean McKee Thompson
Published by Beacon Press, Inc., Boston

 One misty moisty morning,
When cloudy was the weather,
I chanced to meet an old man,
Clothed all in leather.
He began to compliment
And I began to grin.
How do you do? And how do you do?
And how do you do again?

Mother Goose

Rain, rain, go away,
Come again another day;
Little Johnny wants to play.

Mother Goose

A SHOWER   Shower came;
In I came;
Blue sky came!

Izembō
From *Little Pictures of Japan*,
arranged by Olive Beaupré Miller
By permission of the arranger and the publishers,
The Book House for Children, Lake Bluff, Illinois

THE RAIN   Rain on the green grass,
And rain on the tree,
And rain on the house-top,
But not upon me!

Unknown
In *Romney Gay's Picture Book of Poems* (Compiled by P. I. Britcher)
Grosset and Dunlap, New York, 1940

RAIN   The rain is raining all around,
It falls on field and tree,
It rains on the umbrellas here,
And on the ships at sea.

Robert Louis Stevenson, *A Child's Garden of Verses*

MUD

Mud is very nice to feel
All squishy-squash between the toes!
I'd rather wade in wiggly mud
Than smell a yellow rose.

Nobody else but the rosebush knows
How nice mud feels
Between the toes.

Polly Chase Boyden
In *Child Life*, April 1930
Copyright 1930 by Rand McNally & Company
By permission of the author

WHO LIKES THE RAIN?

"I," said the duck, "I call it fun,
For I have my little red rubbers on;
They make a cunning three-toed track
In the soft, cool mud. Quack! Quack! Quack!"

Clara Doty Bates

SPRING RAIN

The storm came up so very quick
    It couldn't have been quicker.
I should have brought my hat along,
    I should have brought my slicker.

My hair is wet, my feet are wet,
    I couldn't be much wetter.
I fell into a river once
    But this is even better.

Marchette Chute, *Rhymes About the City*
Copyright 1946 by The Macmillan Company
and used with their permission

371

GALOSHES

Susie's galoshes
Make splishes and sploshes
And slooshes and sloshes,
As Susie steps slowly
Along in the slush.

They stamp and they tramp
On the ice and concrete,
They get stuck in the muck and the mud;
But Susie likes much best to hear

The slippery slush
As it slooshes and sloshes,
And splishes and sploshes,
All round her galoshes!

Rhoda W. Bacmeister, *Stories to Begin On*
Published and copyright 1940 by E. P. Dutton & Co., Inc., New York

U is for Umbrellas
    That bloom in rainy weather,
Like many-colored mushrooms,
    Sprouting upward altogether.
How useful an umbrella is!
    But still I often wonder
If a roof on stormy evenings
    Isn't nicer to be under.

Phyllis McGinley, *All Around the Town*
Copyright 1948 by Phyllis McGinley
Reprinted by permission of J. B. Lippincott Company

THE UMBRELLA BRIGADE

"Pitter patter!" falls the rain
On the school-room window-pane.
Such a plashing! such a dashing!
Will it e'er be dry again?
Down the gutter rolls a flood,
And the crossing's deep in mud;
And the puddles! oh, the puddles
Are a sight to stir one's blood!

Chorus.   But let it rain
      Tree-toads and frogs,
      Muskets and pitchforks,
      Kittens and dogs!
      Dash away! plash away!
      Who is afraid?
      Here we go,
      The Umbrella Brigade!

Pull the boots up to the knee!
Tie the hoods on merrily!
Such a hustling! such a jostling!
Out of breath with fun are we.
Clatter, clatter, down the street,
Greeting every one we meet,
With our laughing and our chaffing,
Which the laughing drops repeat.

Chorus.   So let it rain
      Tree-toads and frogs,
      Muskets and pitchforks,
      Kittens and dogs!
      Dash away! plash away!
      Who is afraid?
      Here we go,
      The Umbrella Brigade!

Laura E. Richards, *Tirra Lirra*
Little, Brown & Company, Boston, 1932

UMBRELLAS

When the rain is raining
  And April days are cool
All the big umbrellas
  Go bumping home from school.
They bump the blowing cloudburst,
  They push the pushing storm.
They leap a muddy puddle
Or get into a huddle
  To keep each other warm.

But who is underneath them
  You really cannot tell
Unless you know the overshoes
  Or rubbers very well
Or the flippy-flop galoshes
With their swishes and their swashes
Or the running rubber boots
With their scampers and their scoots. . . .

Oh, when the rain is raining
  And April days are cool
I like to watch umbrellas
  Come bumping home from school!
I like to watch and wonder
Who's hiding halfway under. . . .

Rowena Bennett, *Story-Teller Poems*

RAIN IN THE NIGHT

Raining, raining,
All night long;
Sometimes loud, sometimes soft,
Just like a song.

374

There'll be rivers in the gutters
And lakes along the street.
It will make our lazy kitty
Wash his little dirty feet.

The roses will wear diamonds
Like kings and queens at court;
But the pansies all get muddy
Because they are so short.

I'll sail my boat tomorrow
In wonderful new places,
But first I'll take my watering-pot
And wash the pansies' faces.

Amelia Josephine Burr
Selected Lyrics of Amelia Josephine Burr
Copyright 1927 by Doubleday & Company, Inc.

VERY LOVELY

Wouldn't it be lovely if the rain came down
Till the water was quite high over all the town?
If the cabs and buses all were set afloat,
And we had to go to school in a little boat?

Wouldn't it be lovely if it still should pour
And we all went up to live on the second floor?
If we saw the butcher sailing up the hill,
And we took the letters in at the window sill?

It's been raining, raining, all the afternoon;
All these things might happen really very soon.
If we woke to-morrow and found they had begun,
Wouldn't it be glorious? *Wouldn't* it be fun?

Rose Fyleman, *Fairies and Chimneys*
Copyright 1920 by Doubleday & Company, Inc., New York
Copyright 1948 by Rose Fyleman
By permission of The Society of Authors
and Messrs. Methuen & Co., Ltd., London

SPRING RAIN

Leaves make a slow
Whispering sound
As down the drops go
Drip to the ground
    Peace, peace, says the tree.

Good wet rain!
Shout happy frogs,
Peepers and big green
Bulls in bogs,
    Lucky, lucky are we!

On a bough above,
Head under wing,
A mourning dove
Waits time to sing.
    Ah me, she sighs, ah me!

Harry Behn, *The Little Hill*
Harcourt, Brace and Company, Inc., New York, Copyright 1949

IT IS RAINING

It is raining.

Where would you like to be in the rain?
Where would you like to be?

I'd like to be on a city street,
where the rain comes down in a driving sheet,
where it wets the houses—roof and wall—
the wagons and horses and autos and all.
That's where I'd like to be in the rain,
that's where I'd like to be.

It is raining.

Where would you like to be in the rain?
Where would you like to be?

I'd like to be in a tall tree top,
where the rain comes dripping, drop, drop, drop,
around on every side:
where it wets the farmer, the barn, the pig,
the cows, the chickens both little and big;
where it batters and beats on a field of wheat
and makes the little birds hide.

It is raining.

Where would you like to be in the rain?
Where would you like to be?

I'd like to be on a ship at sea,
where everything's wet as wet can be
and the waves are rolling high,
where sailors are pulling the ropes and singing,
and wind's in the rigging and salt spray's stinging,
and round us sea gulls cry.
On a dipping skimming ship at sea—
that's where I'd like to be in the rain;
that's where I'd like to be!

Lucy Sprague Mitchell

In Another Here and Now Story Book
Published and Copyright 1937 by E. P. Dutton & Co., Inc., New York

CITY RAIN

Rain in the city!
  I love to see it fall
Slantwise where the buildings crowd
  Red brick and all.
Streets of shiny wetness
  Where the taxis go,
With people and umbrellas all
  Bobbing to and fro.

Rain in the city!
  I love to hear it drip
When I am cosy in my room
  Snug as any ship,
With toys spread on the table,
  With a picture book or two,
And the rain like a rumbling tune that sings
  Through everything I do.

Rachel Field, *Taxis and Toadstools*

THE RAINS OF SPRING

The rains of spring
Which hang to the branches
  Of the green willow,
Look like pearls upon a string.

Lady Ise
From *Little Pictures of Japan,*
arranged by Olive Beaupré Miller
By permission of the arranger and the publishers,
The Book House for Children, Lake Bluff, Illinois

APRIL RAIN SONG

Let the rain kiss you.
Let the rain beat upon your head with silver liquid drops.
Let the rain sing you a lullaby.

The rain makes still pools on the sidewalk.
The rain makes running pools in the gutter.
The rain plays a little sleep-song on our roof at night—

And I love the rain.

Langston Hughes, *The Dream-Keeper*
Reprinted by permission of Alfred A. Knopf, Inc.
Copyright 1932 by Alfred A. Knopf, Inc.

RAIN RIDERS

Last night I heard a *rat-tat-too;*
  'Twas not a drum-beat, that was plain;
I listened long, and then I knew
  It was the Riders of the Rain.

But with the rising of the dawn
  There was no sound of any hoofs;
The Riders of the Rain had gone
  To tramp on other children's roofs.

Clinton Scollard
In *St. Nicholas,* 1922
Copyright 1922 by the Century Company
Reprinted by permission of Appleton-Century-Crofts, Inc.

IN

TIME

OF

SILVER

RAIN

In time of silver rain
The earth
Puts forth new life again,
Green grasses grow
And flowers lift their heads,
And over all the plain
The wonder spreads
    Of life,
    Of life,
    Of life!

In time of silver rain
The butterflies
Lift silken wings
To catch a rainbow cry,
And trees put forth
New leaves to sing
In joy beneath the sky
As down the roadway
Passing boys and girls
Go singing, too,
In time of silver rain
    When spring
    And life
    Are new.

Langston Hughes, *Fields of Wonder*
Reprinted by permission of Alfred A. Knopf, Inc.
Copyright 1947 by Langston Hughes

THE RAIN

I hear leaves drinking rain;
   I hear rich leaves on top
Giving the poor beneath
   Drop after drop;
'Tis a sweet noise to hear
These green leaves drinking near.

And when the Sun comes out,
   After this rain shall stop,
A wondrous light will fill
   Each dark, round drop;
I hope the Sun shines bright;
'Twill be a lovely sight.

William Henry Davies, *Collected Poems*
Jonathan Cape & Harrison Smith, New York, 1929

FOG

The fog comes
on little cat feet.

It sits looking
over harbor and city
on silent haunches
and then moves on.

Carl Sandburg, *Chicago Poems*
Copyright 1916 by Henry Holt and Company, Inc.
Copyright 1944 by Carl Sandburg
Used by permission of the publishers

THE FOG

I saw the fog grow thick,
　Which soon made blind my ken;
It made tall men of boys,
　And giants of tall men.

It clutched my throat, I coughed;
　Nothing was in my head
Except two heavy eyes
　Like balls of burning lead.

And when it grew so black
　That I could know no place,
I lost all judgment then,
　Of distance and of space.

The street lamps, and the lights
　Upon the halted cars,
Could either be on earth
　Or be the heavenly stars.

A man passed by me close,
　I asked my way, he said,
'Come, follow me, my friend'—
　I followed where he led.

He rapped the stones in front,
　'Trust me' he said 'and come';
I followed like a child—
　A blind man led me home.

William Henry Davies
The Collected Poems of W. H. Davies

Reprinted by permission of the publishers,
Jonathan Cape Limited, London
and Mrs. H. M. Davies

The tide in the river,
The tide in the river,
The tide in the river runs deep.
I saw a shiver
Pass over the river
As the tide turned in its sleep.

Eleanor Farjeon, *Gypsy and Ginger*
Copyright 1920, 1948 by Eleanor Farjeon

Boats sail on the rivers,
    And ships sail on the seas;
But clouds that sail across the sky
    Are prettier far than these.

There are bridges on the rivers,
    As pretty as you please;
But the bow that bridges heaven,
    And overtops the trees,
And builds a road from earth to sky,
    Is prettier far than these.

Christina Georgina Rossetti, *Sing-Song*

THE RAINBOW

I saw the lovely arch
Of Rainbow span the sky,
The gold sun burning
As the rain swept by.

In bright-ringed solitude
The showery foliage shone
One lovely moment,
And the Bow was gone.

Walter de la Mare, *Collected Poems, 1901–1918*

My heart leaps up when I behold
  A rainbow in the sky:
So was it when my life began;
So is it now I am a man;
So be it when I shall grow old,
  Or let me die!

William Wordsworth

ROUND THE CLOCK

Every evening after play
When the sunshine goes away,
It's nice to say,
Thank you for this happy day.

THE BIG CLOCK

Slowly ticks the big clock;
Tick-tock, tick-tock!
But Cuckoo clock ticks double quick;
Tick-a-tock-a, tick-a-tock-a,
Tick-a-tock-a, tick!

Unknown

TICKING CLOCKS

The cuckoo clock on the nursery wall
Has a voice that is woody and brown and small,
And all day long in happy rhyme
Its ticks are saying, *Plenty of Time,*
There's always plenty of Time.

On the mantel over the fireplace
The marble clock with the gilded face
And chimes as sweet as a sea-drowned bell
Says over and over, *Time will tell,*
Yes, Time will always tell.

The old hall clock with the pendulum
Beats every hour like a drum.
Heavy and deep, from far inside,
Hear how it booms out, *Time and Tide,*
Solemnly, Time and Tide.

Rachel Field, *Poems*

Bell horses, bell horses, what time of day?
One o'clock, two o'clock, three and away.

Mother Goose

The cock doth crow
 To let you know,
If you be wise,
'Tis time to rise.

Mother Goose

Cocks crow in the morn
   To tell us to rise,
And he who lies late
   Will never be wise;
For early to bed
   And early to rise,
Is the way to be healthy
   And wealthy and wise.

Mother Goose

SINGING-TIME   I wake in the morning early
And always, the very first thing,
I poke out my head and I sit up in bed
And I sing and I sing and I sing.

Rose Fyleman, *The Fairy Green*

WAKING TIME

At four o'clock in the morning,
The cockerels wake, they do,
    With a "Cocker-doo-dle,
    Cocker-doo-dle,
Cocker-doo-dle-doo!"

At five o'clock in the morning,
The thrushes wake, they do,
    With a "Pretty-sweet!
    Oh, pretty-sweet!
The sky is rose-and-blue!"

At six o'clock in the morning,
The blackbirds wake, they do,
    With a "What's to eat?
    Oh, what's to eat?
I'd like a worm or two!"

At seven o'clock in the morning,
The mothers wake, they do,
    With a "Here's the honey,
    And here's the bread,
And milk all sweet and new!"

At eight o'clock in the morning,
The children wake, they do,
    With a "Where's my sock?"
    And "Where's my smock?"
And "I can't find my left shoe!"

Ivy O. Eastwick

Reprinted by permission from *Jack and Jill*, June 1946

A SUMMER MORNING

I saw dawn creep across the sky,
And all the gulls go flying by.
I saw the sea put on its dress
Of blue mid-summer loveliness,
And heard the trees begin to stir
Green arms of pine and juniper.
I heard the wind call out and say:
"Get up, my dear, it is to-day!"

Rachel Field, *The Pointed People*
The Macmillan Company, New York, 1930

THE SUN

I told the Sun that I was glad,
    I'm sure I don't know why;
Somehow the pleasant way he had
    Of shining in the sky,
Just put a notion in my head
    That wouldn't it be fun
If, walking on the hill, I said
    "I'm happy" to the Sun.

John Drinkwater, *All About Me*
Reprinted by permission of and arrangement with
Houghton Mifflin Company, the authorized publishers

SUNRISE

The first gray smoke of daylight blurs
The morning star. The first bird stirs.

The bright sun bubbles from the sea
And sprays its gold on every tree.

Rowena Bennett
From the piano solo *Sunrise* by Berenice Benson Bentley
Copyright 1938 by Summy-Birchard Publishing Company
By permission of the author

R is for the Restaurant—
  A really special treat.
(We do respect the relative
  Who takes us there to eat.)
The waiters rush with plates of rolls,
  They run to hold one's chair,
And always seem
To read ice-cream
  Upon the bill-of-fare.

Phyllis McGinley, *All Around the Town*

EUNICE

IN THE

EVENING

What is so nice in the dining room
Is—Everybody's There!
Daddy on the long settee—
A child in every chair—
Mama pouring cocoa in
The little cups of blue.
(And each of us has leave to take
A ginger cookie, too.)

Gwendolyn Brooks, *Bronzeville Boys and Girls*

ANIMAL
CRACKERS

Animal crackers, and cocoa to drink,
That is the finest of suppers, I think;
When I'm grown up and can have what I please
I think I shall always insist upon these.
What do *you* choose when you're offered a treat?
When Mother says, "What would you like best to eat?"
Is it waffles and syrup, or cinnamon toast?
It's cocoa and animals that *I* love most!

The kitchen's the cosiest place that I know:
The kettle is singing, the stove is aglow,
And there in the twilight, how jolly to see
The cocoa and animals waiting for me.

Daddy and Mother dine later in state,
With Mary to cook for them, Susan to wait;
But they don't have nearly as much fun as I
Who eat in the kitchen with Nurse standing by;
And Daddy once said, he would like to be me
Having cocoa and animals once more for tea!

Christopher Morley, *Songs for a Little House*
Copyright 1917, 1945 by Christopher Morley
Published by J. B. Lippincott Company

EVENING

Now the drowsy sunshine
Slides far away

Into the happy morning
Of someone else's day.

THIS

IS

MY ROCK

This is my rock,
And here I run
To steal the secret of the sun;

This is my rock,
And here come I
Before the night has swept the sky;

This is my rock,
This is the place
I meet the evening face to face.

THIS
HAPPY
DAY

Every morning when the sun
Comes smiling up on everyone,
It's lots of fun
To say good morning to the sun.
    Good morning, Sun!

Every evening after play
When the sunshine goes away,
It's nice to say,
Thank you for this happy day,
    This happy day!

Harry Behn, *The Little Hill*
Harcourt, Brace and Company, Inc., New York, Copyright 1949

W's for Windows.
    Watch them welcome in the night.
How they twinkle, twinkle, twinkle
    With the waning of the light!
There's nothing half so wonderful
    In all the wond'rous town
As a million winking Windows
    When the dusk is coming down.

Phyllis McGinley, *All Around the Town*
Copyright 1948 by Phyllis McGinley
Reprinted by permission of J. B. Lippincott Company

THE PARK

I'm glad that I
    Live near a park

For in the winter
    After dark

The park lights shine
    As bright and still

As dandelions
    On a hill.

James S. Tippett, *I Live in a City*
Copyright 1927 by Harper & Brothers

SUMMER EVENING

The sandy cat by the Farmer's chair
Mews at his knee for dainty fare;
Old Rover in his moss-greened house
Mumbles a bone, and barks at a mouse.
In the dewy fields the cattle lie
Chewing the cud 'neath a fading sky;
Dobbin at manger pulls his hay:
Gone is another summer's day.

Walter de la Mare, *Rhymes and Verses*
Published by Henry Holt & Company, Inc., New York, 1947
By permission of the literary trustees of Walter de la Mare
and The Society of Authors, London, as their representatives

LIGHT THE LAMPS UP, LAMPLIGHTER!

Light the lamps up, Lamplighter,
The people are in the street—
Without a light
They have no sight,
And where will they plant their feet?
Some will tread in the gutter,
And some in the mud—oh dear!
Light the lamps up, Lamplighter,
Because the night is here.

Light the candles, Grandmother,
The children are going to bed—
Without a wick
They'll stumble and stick,
And where will they lay their head?
Some will lie on the staircase,
And some in the hearth—oh dear!
Light the candles, Grandmother,
Because the night is here.

Light the stars up, Gabriel,
The cherubs are out to fly—
If heaven is blind
How will they find
Their way across the sky?
Some will splash in the Milky Way,
Or bump on the moon—oh dear!
Light the stars up, Gabriel,
Because the night is here.

Eleanor Farjeon, *Poems for Children*

SETTING THE TABLE

Evenings
When the house is quiet
I delight
To spread the white
Smooth cloth and put the flowers on the table.

I place the knives and forks around
Without a sound.
I light the candles.

I love to see
Their small reflected torches shine
Against the greenness of the vine
And garden.

Is that the mignonette, I wonder,
Smells so sweet?

And then I call them in to eat.

Dorothy Aldis, *Any Spring*
Minton, Balch and Company, New York, 1933
Copyright 1933 by Dorothy Aldis

EVENING HYMN

The day is done;
The lamps are lit;
Woods-ward the birds are flown.
Shadows draw close,—
Peace be unto this house.

The cloth is fair;
The food is set.
God's night draw near.
Quiet and love and peace
Be to this, our rest, our place.

Elizabeth Madox Roberts, *Song in the Meadow*
Copyright 1940 by Elizabeth Madox Roberts
Reprinted by permission of The Viking Press, Inc., New York

SNOW TOWARD EVENING

Suddenly the sky turned gray,
The day,
Which had been bitter and chill,
Grew intensely soft and still.
Quietly
From some invisible blossoming tree
Millions of petals cool and white
Drifted and blew,
Lifted and flew,
Fell with the falling night.

Melville Cane, *January Garden*
Harcourt, Brace and Company, Inc., New York, Copyright 1926

FINIS

Night is come,
   Owls are out;
Beetles hum
   Round about.

Children snore
   Safe in bed,
Nothing more
   Need be said.

Sir Henry Newbolt
In *Goodchild's Garland*
Elkin Matthews, London
Used by permission of the executors of the Estate of Sir Henry Newbolt

CHECK

The Night was creeping on the ground!
She crept and did not make a sound,

Until she reached the tree: And then
She covered it, and stole again

Along the grass beside the wall!
—I heard the rustling of her shawl

As she threw blackness everywhere
Along the sky, the ground, the air,

And in the room where I was hid!
But, no matter what she did

To everything that was without,
She could not put my candle out!

So I stared at the Night! And she
Stared back solemnly at me!

James Stephens, *Rocky Road to Dublin*
Copyright 1915, 1943 by The Macmillan Company
and used with their permission
(Also in *Collected Poems* by James Stephens
Used by permission of the author and Macmillan & Co., Ltd., London)

Star-light, star-bright
First star I've seen tonight;
I wish I may, I wish I might
Get the wish I wish tonight.

The American Mother Goose (Compiled by Ray Wood)
Copyright 1940 by J. B. Lippincott Company

THE STAR

Twinkle, twinkle, little star,
How I wonder what you are!
Up above the world so high,
Like a diamond in the sky.

Jane Taylor

ESCAPE

AT

BEDTIME

The lights from the parlour and kitchen shone out
   Through the blinds and the windows and bars;
And high overhead and all moving about,
   There were thousands of millions of stars.

There ne'er were such thousands of leaves on a tree,
   Nor of people in church or the park,
As the crowds of the stars that looked down upon me,
   And that glittered and winked in the dark.

The Dog, and the Plough, and the Hunter, and all,
   And the Star of the Sailor, and Mars,
These shone in the sky, and the pail by the wall
   Would be half full of water and stars.

They saw me at last, and they chased me with cries,
   And they soon had me packed into bed;
But the glory kept shining and bright in my eyes,
   And the stars going round in my head.

Robert Louis Stevenson, *A Child's Garden of Verses*

UNTIL WE BUILT A CABIN

When we lived in a city
(three flights up and down)
I never dreamed how many stars
could show above a town.

When we moved to a village
where lighted streets were few,
I thought I could see ALL the stars,
but, oh, I never knew—

Until we built a cabin
where hills are high and far,
I never knew how many
many
stars there really are!

Aileen Fisher, *That's Why*
Published by Thomas Nelson & Sons, New York, 1946
By permission of the author

THE FALLING STAR

I saw a star slide down the sky,
Blinding the north as it went by,
Too burning and too quick to hold,
Too lovely to be bought or sold,
Good only to make wishes on
And then forever to be gone.

Sara Teasdale, *Stars To-Night*
Copyright 1930 by Sara T. Filsinger
and used with the permission of The Macmillan Company

STARS

Alone in the night
  On a dark hill
With pines around me
  Spicy and still,

And a heaven full of stars
  Over my head,
White and topaz
  And misty red;

Myriads with beating
  Hearts of fire
That aeons
  Cannot vex or tire;

Up the dome of heaven
  Like a great hill,
I watch them marching
  Stately and still,

And I know that I
  Am honored to be
Witness
  Of so much majesty.

Sara Teasdale, *Flame and Shadow*
Copyright 1920, 1948 by The Macmillan Company
and used with their permission

MOON-COME-OUT

Moon-Come-Out
And Sun-Go-In,
Here's a soft blanket
To cuddle your chin.

Moon-Go-In
And Sun-Come-Out,
Throw off the blanket
And bustle about.

Eleanor Farjeon, *Over the Garden Wall*
Copyright 1933 by Eleanor Farjeon
Reprinted by permission of J. B. Lippincott Company
(Also in *Poems for Children* by Eleanor Farjeon
Published by J. B. Lippincott Company, Philadelphia and New York
Copyright 1951 by Eleanor Farjeon)

 I see the moon,
And the moon sees me;
God bless the moon,
And God bless me.

Unknown

MOON

SONG

There is a star that runs very fast,
That goes pulling the moon
Through the tops of the poplars.
It is all in silver,
The tall star:
The moon rolls goldenly along
Out of breath.
Mr. Moon, does he make you hurry?

Hilda Conkling, *Poems by a Little Girl*
Copyright 1920 by J. B. Lippincott Company

402

THE WHITE WINDOW

The Moon comes every night to peep
    Through the window where I lie,
And I pretend to be asleep;
    But I watch the Moon as it goes by,
And it never makes a sound.

It stands and stares, and then it goes
    To the house that's next to me,
Stealing on its tippy-toes,
    To peep at folk asleep maybe;
And it never makes a sound.

James Stephens, *Rocky Road to Dublin*
Copyright 1915, 1943 by The Macmillan Company
and used with their permission
(Also in *Collected Poems* by James Stephens
Used by permission of the author and Macmillan & Co., Ltd., London)

FULL MOON

One night as Dick lay fast asleep,
    Into his drowsy eyes
A great still light began to creep
    From out the silent skies.
It was the lovely moon's, for when
    He raised his dreamy head,
Her surge of silver filled the pane
    And streamed across his bed.
So, for awhile, each gazed at each—
    Dick and the solemn moon—
Till, climbing slowly on her way,
    She vanished, and was gone.

Walter de la Mare, *Collected Poems, 1901–1918*
Copyright 1920 by Henry Holt and Company, Inc.
Copyright 1948 by Walter de la Mare
Reprinted by permission of the publishers
(Also in *Rhymes and Verses* by Walter de la Mare
Published by Henry Holt and Company, Inc., New York, 1947)

SILVER

Slowly, silently, now the moon
Walks the night in her silver shoon;
This way, and that, she peers, and sees
Silver fruit upon silver trees;
One by one the casements catch
Her beams beneath the silvery thatch;
Couched in his kennel, like a log,
With paws of silver sleeps the dog;
From their shadowy cote the white breasts peep
Of doves in a silver-feathered sleep;
A harvest mouse goes scampering by,
With silver claws, and silver eye;
And moveless fish in the water gleam,
By silver reeds in a silver stream.

Walter de la Mare, *Collected Poems, 1901–1918*

LAST
SONG

To the Sun
Who has shone
   All day,
To the Moon
Who has gone
   Away,
To the milk-white,
Silk-white,
Lily-white Star
A fond goodnight
Wherever you are.

James Guthrie

ROUND
THE
CALENDAR

Spring is showery, flowery, bowery;
Summer: hoppy, croppy, poppy;
Autumn: wheezy, sneezy, freezy;
Winter: slippy, drippy, nippy.

How many days has my baby to play?
　　Saturday, Sunday, Monday,
Tuesday, Wednesday, Thursday, Friday,
　　Saturday, Sunday, Monday.

Mother Goose

**OPEN
THE
DOOR**

Open the door and who'll come in?
　　Who'll come in?
　　Who'll come in?
Open the door and who'll come in,
　　So early Monday morning?

My little pussycat, she'll come in,
Rubbing her fur against my shin.
She'll arch her back and she'll step right in,
　　So early Monday morning.

Open the door and who'll come in?
　　Who'll come in?
　　Who'll come in?
Open the door and who'll come in,
　　So early Tuesday morning?

My little puppy dog, he'll come in,
Mud on his paws and mud on his chin.
He'll bounce and he'll pounce as he dashes in,
　　So early Tuesday morning.

Open the door and who'll come in?
　　Who'll come in?
　　Who'll come in?
Open the door and who'll come in,
　　So early Wednesday morning?

My little Dicky bird, he'll come in,
His eyes so black and his legs so thin.

He'll fly to his cage and he'll pop right in,
   So early Wednesday morning.

Open the door and who do you see?
   Who do you see?
   Who do you see?
Open the door and who do you see,
   So early Thursday morning?

Beulah the pony is visiting me,
Nuzzling her nose against my knee,
Asking for sugar, as plain as can be,
   So early Thursday morning.

Open the door and who'll be there?
   Who'll be there?
   Who'll be there?
Open the door and who'll be there,
   So early Friday morning?

The Skillipot turtles, a tiny pair,
Their shells so hard and their heads so bare.
It takes them an hour to get anywhere
   So early Friday morning.

Open the door and what do you know?
   What do you know?
   What do you know?
Open the door and what do you know,
   So early Saturday morning?

My beautiful bunnies are white as snow,
And their pink little noses wiggle so.
Three pretty hops, and in they go,
   So early Saturday morning.

Marion Edey and Dorothy Grider, *Open the Door*
Copyright 1949 by Marion Edey and Dorothy Grider
Used by permission of the publishers, Charles Scribner's Sons

TELEGRAM

I NEVER got a telegram before;
But I went to the big front door,
And here was a man
Who wanted to see
Master Jonathan Blake!
So I said, "That's me."
And to make things clear,
He said, "Please sign here."
I never got a telegram before,
But I'd like to get at least a million more.

I never got a "wire" in my life;
So I sliced this one open with a knife.
Mother said most men
Prefer to use a cutter,
Since the knife I found
Was designed for butter.
But I never got a "wire" in my life!
So *naturally* I sliced it with a knife.

I never got a telegram before;
And when I went to the big front door,
It said: "Congratulations
On being six today
Every one of us loves you
That's all we can say."
I never got a telegram before,
But I'd like to get at least a *million* more!

William Wise, *Jonathan Blake*

Published by Alfred A. Knopf, Inc., New York
Copyright © 1956 by William Wise
By permission of the author and the publisher

A BIRTHDAY

Did you ever think how queer
That, every day all through the year,
Someone has a frosted cake,
And candles for a birthday's sake?

Rachel Field, *A Little Book of Days*
Copyright 1927 by Doubleday & Company, Inc., New York
By permission of the publisher

January brings the snow,
  Makes our feet and fingers glow.
February brings the rain,
  Thaws the frozen lake again.
March brings breezes loud and shrill,
  Stirs the dancing daffodil.

April brings the primrose sweet,
  Scatters daisies at our feet.
May brings flocks of pretty lambs,
  Skipping by their fleecy dams.
June brings tulips, lilies, roses,
  Fills the children's hands with posies.

Hot July brings cooling showers,
  Apricots and gillyflowers.
August brings the sheaves of corn,
  Then the harvest home is borne.
Warm September brings the fruit,
  Sportsmen then begin to shoot.

Fresh October brings the pheasant,
  Then to gather nuts is pleasant.
Dull November brings the blast,
  Then the leaves are whirling fast.
Chill December brings the sleet,
  Blazing fire and Christmas treat.

Mother Goose

FOUR SEASONS

Springtime is a green time
    When seedlings start their growing.
Summertime's a rainbow time
    When many blooms are blowing.
Autumntime's a brown time
    When seeds are ripe for sowing;
But wintertime's a white time
(It is the flowers' nighttime)
    When stars of frost are glowing.

Rowena Bennett
In *Jack and Jill,* January 1947
Copyright 1947 by The Curtis Publishing Company

Spring is showery, flowery, bowery;
Summer: hoppy, croppy, poppy;
Autumn: wheezy, sneezy, freezy;
Winter: slippy, drippy, nippy.

Mother Goose

Monday morning back to school
Fool fool fool fool
Monday morning back we go
No No No No
Monday morning summer's gone
John John John John
Monday morning what a pain
Jane Jane Jane Jane

David McCord, *Far and Few*
Copyright 1929, 1931, 1952 by David McCord
By permission of Little, Brown & Company, Boston

SEPTEMBER

The goldenrod is yellow;
 The corn is turning brown;
The trees in apple orchards
 With fruit are bending down.

The gentian's bluest fringes
 Are curling in the sun;
In dusty pods the milkweed
 Its hidden silk has spun.

The sedges flaunt their harvest,
 In every meadow nook;
And asters by the brook-side
 Make asters in the brook.

From dewy lanes at morning
 The grapes' sweet odors rise;
At noon the roads all flutter
 With yellow butterflies.

By all these lovely tokens
 September days are here,
With summer's best of weather,
 And autumn's best of cheer.

Helen Hunt Jackson, *Poems*

SEPTEMBER

A road like brown ribbon,
A sky that is blue,
A forest of green
With that sky peeping through.

Asters, deep purple,
A grasshopper's call,
Today it is summer,
Tomorrow is fall.

Edwina Fallis
In *Sung under the Silver Umbrella*
The Macmillan Company, New York, 1935

411

The morns are meeker than they were,
The nuts are getting brown;
The berry's cheek is plumper,
The rose is out of town.

The maple wears a gayer scarf,
The field a scarlet gown.
Lest I should be old-fashioned,
I'll put a trinket on.

Emily Dickinson, *The Poems of Emily Dickinson*
Little, Brown & Company, Boston, 1939

AUTUMN FIRES

In the other gardens
    And all up the vale,
From the autumn bonfires
    See the smoke trail!

Pleasant summer over
    And all the summer flowers.
The red fire blazes,
    The gray smoke towers.

Sing a song of seasons!
    Something bright in all!
Flowers in the summer,
    Fires in the fall!

Robert Louis Stevenson, *A Child's Garden of Verses*

DOWN! DOWN!

Down, down!
Yellow and brown
The leaves are falling over the town.

Eleanor Farjeon, *Joan's Door*

Copyright 1926 by J. B. Lippincott Company
(Also in *Poems for Children* by Eleanor Farjeon
Published by J. B. Lippincott Company, Philadelphia and New York
Copyright 1951 by Eleanor Farjeon)

AUTUMN WOODS

I like the woods
    In autumn
When dry leaves hide the ground,
When the trees are bare
And the wind sweeps by
With a lonesome rushing sound.

I can rustle the leaves
    In autumn
And I can make a bed
In the thick dry leaves
That have fallen
From the bare trees
Overhead.

James S. Tippett, *A World to Know*
Copyright 1933 by Harper & Brothers

THE CITY OF FALLING LEAVES

Leaves fall,
Brown leaves,
Yellow leaves streaked with brown.
They fall,
Flutter,
Fall again.
The brown leaves,
And the streaked yellow leaves,
Loosen on their branches
And drift slowly downwards.
One,
One, two, three,
One, two, five.
All Venice is a falling of Autumn leaves—
Brown,
And yellow streaked with brown.

Amy Lowell, *Men, Women and Ghosts*
Reprinted by permission of and arrangement with
Houghton Mifflin Company, the authorized publishers

OCTOBER

The summer is over,
   The trees are all bare,
There is mist in the garden
   And frost in the air.
The meadows are empty
   And gathered the sheaves—
But isn't it lovely
   Kicking up leaves!

John from the garden
   Has taken the chairs;
It's dark in the evening
   And cold on the stairs.
Winter is coming
   And everyone grieves—
But isn't it lovely
   Kicking up leaves!

Rose Fyleman, *Gay Go Up*

APPLE SONG

The apples are seasoned
And ripe and sound.
Gently they fall
On the yellow ground.

The apples are stored
In the dusky bin
Where hardly a glimmer
Of light creeps in.

414

In the firelit, winter
Nights, they'll be
The clear sweet taste
Of a summer tree!

Frances Frost, *The Pool in the Meadow*
Published by Houghton Mifflin Company, Boston, 1933
By permission of the author

SPLINTER

The voice of the last cricket
across the first frost
is one kind of good-by.
It is so thin a splinter of singing.

Carl Sandburg, *Good Morning, America*
Harcourt, Brace and Company, Inc., New York, Copyright 1928

HALLOWE'EN

The moon is round as a jack-o'-lantern;
The trees blow black and bare;
And we go creeping with spooky giggles
Through the chill ghostly air.

Whose shadow is that on the haunted ground?
Who's hiding behind that tree?
Oh, down the tree runs my bad black kitten,
And the shadow is only me!

Frances Frost, *The Little Whistler*
Whittlesey House, McGraw-Hill Book Company, Inc., New York, 1949

415

MY BROTHER

My brother is inside the sheet
That gave that awful shout.
I know because those are his feet
So brown and sticking out.

And that's his head that waggles there
And his eyes peeking through—
So I can laugh, so I don't care:
"Ha!" I say. "It's you."

Dorothy Aldis, *Hop, Skip and Jump*
Minton, Balch and Company, New York, 1934
Copyright 1934 by Dorothy Aldis

HALLOWEEN

"Granny, I saw a witch go by,
I saw two, I saw three!
I heard their skirts go swish, swish, swish——"

"Child, 'twas leaves against the sky,
And the autumn wind in the tree."

"Granny, broomsticks they bestrode,
Their hats were black as tar,
And buckles twinkled on their shoes——"

"You saw but shadows on the road,
The sparkle of a star."

"Granny, all their heels were red,
Their cats were big as sheep.
I heard a bat say to an owl——"

"Child, you must go straight to bed,
'Tis time you were asleep."

416

"Granny, I saw men in green,
Their eyes shone fiery red,
Their heads were yellow pumpkins——"

  "Now you've told me what you've seen,
  WILL you go to bed?"

"Granny?"

  "Well?"

"Don't you believe——?"

  "What?"

"What I've seen?
Don't you know it's Halloween?"

Marie A. Lawson

In *Child Life,* October 1936
Copyright 1936 by Rand McNally & Co., Chicago
By permission of the Estate of Marie A. Lawson

BLACK

AND

GOLD

Everything is black and gold,
  Black and gold, tonight:
Yellow pumpkins, yellow moon,
  Yellow candlelight;

Jet-black cat with golden eyes,
  Shadows black as ink,
Firelight blinking in the dark
  With a yellow blink.

Black and gold, black and gold,
  Nothing in between—
When the world turns black and gold,
  Then it's Halloween!

Nancy Byrd Turner
In *Child Life,* October 1929
Copyright 1929 by Rand McNally & Company
By permission of the author

THEME IN YELLOW

I spot the hills
With yellow balls in autumn.
I light the prairie cornfields
Orange and tawny gold clusters
And I am called pumpkins.
On the last of October
When dusk is fallen
Children join hands
And circle round me
Singing ghost songs
And love to the harvest moon;
I am a jack-o'-lantern
With terrible teeth
And the children know
I am fooling.

HALLOWE'EN

Tonight is the night
When dead leaves fly
Like witches on switches
Across the sky,
When elf and sprite
Flit through the night
On a moony sheen.

Tonight is the night
When leaves make a sound
Like a gnome in his home
Under the ground,
When spooks and trolls

Creep out of holes
Mossy and green.

Tonight is the night
When pumpkins stare
Through sheaves and leaves
Everywhere,
When ghoul and ghost
And goblin host
Dance round their queen.
It's Hallowe'en!

Harry Behn, *The Little Hill*
Harcourt, Brace and Company, Inc., New York, Copyright 1949

THIS IS

HALLOWEEN

Goblins on the doorstep,
  Phantoms in the air,
Owls on witches' gateposts
  Giving stare for stare,
Cats on flying broomsticks,
  Bats against the moon,
Stirrings round of fate-cakes
  With a solemn spoon,
Whirling apple parings,
  Figures draped in sheets
Dodging, disappearing,
  Up and down the streets,
Jack-o'-lanterns grinning,
  Shadows on a screen,
Shrieks and starts and laughter—
  This is Halloween!

Dorothy Brown Thompson
In *Child Life*, October 1941
Copyright 1941 by Rand McNally & Company
By permission of the author

419

THE RIDE-BY-NIGHTS

Up on their brooms the Witches stream,
Crooked and black in the crescent's gleam,
One foot high, and one foot low,
Bearded, cloaked, and cowled, they go.
'Neath Charlie's Wane they twitter and tweet,
And away they swarm 'neath the Dragon's feet,
With a whoop and a flutter they swing and sway,
And surge pell-mell down the Milky Way.
Between the legs of the glittering Chair
They hover and squeak in the empty air.
Then round they swoop past the glimmering Lion
To where Sirius barks behind huge Orion;
Up, then, and over to wheel amain
Under the silver, and home again.

Walter de la Mare, *Collected Poems, 1901–1918*

NOVEMBER

Bracken on the hillside
frosted and white.
Garden all brown.
Storm windows tight.
Screens in the attic.
Barn full of hay.
Bathing suits mothproofed,
folded away.
And coming 'round the corner
on his tip, tip toes,
Winter, Winter, Winter
with a cold red nose!

Aileen Fisher, *That's Why*

THE LAST WORD OF A BLUEBIRD

(As Told to a Child)

As I went out a Crow
In a low voice said 'Oh,
I was looking for you.
How do you do?
I just came to tell you
To tell Lesley (will you?)
That her little Bluebird
Wanted me to bring word
That the north wind last night
That made the stars bright
And made ice on the trough
Almost made him cough
His tail feathers off.
He just had to fly!
But he sent her Good-by,
And said to be good,
And wear her red hood,
And look for skunk tracks
In the snow with an ax—
And do everything!
And perhaps in the spring
He would come back and sing.'

Robert Frost, *Mountain Interval*

SOMETHING TOLD THE WILD GEESE

Something told the wild geese
  It was time to go.
Though the fields lay golden
  Something whispered, "Snow."
Leaves were green and stirring,
  Berries, luster-glossed,
But beneath warm feathers
  Something cautioned, "Frost."
All the sagging orchards
  Steamed with amber spice,
But each wild breast stiffened
  At remembered ice.
Something told the wild geese
  It was time to fly—
Summer sun was on their wings,
  Winter in their cry.

Rachel Field, *Branches Green*

THANKSGIVING MAGIC

Thanksgiving Day I like to see
Our cook perform her witchery.
She turns a pumpkin into pie
As easily as you or I
Can wave a hand or wink an eye.
She takes leftover bread and muffin
And changes them to turkey stuffin'.
She changes cranberries to sauce
And meats to stews and stews to broths,
And when she mixes gingerbread
It turns into a man instead
With frosting collar 'round his throat
And raisin buttons down his coat.
Oh, some like magic made by wands,
    And some read magic out of books,
And some like fairy spells and charms
    But I like magic made by cooks!

Rowena Bennett
In *Child Life*, November 1944
Copyright 1944 by Child Life, Inc.
By permission of the author

THE MITTEN SONG

"Thumbs in the thumb-place,
Fingers all together!"
This is the song
We sing in mitten-weather.
When it is cold,
It doesn't matter whether
Mittens are wool,
Or made of finest leather.
This is the song
We sing in mitten-weather:
"Thumbs in the thumb-place,
Fingers all together!"

Marie Louise Allen
In *Sung under the Silver Umbrella*
The Macmillan Company, New York, 1935

ICE

When it is the winter time
I run up the street
And I make the ice laugh
With my little feet—
"Crickle, crackle, crickle
Crrreeet, crrreeet, crrreeet."

Dorothy Aldis, *Everything and Anything*
Minton, Balch and Company, New York, 1927
Copyright 1925, 1926, 1927 by Dorothy Aldis

FIRST SNOW

Snow makes whiteness where it falls.
The bushes look like popcorn-balls.
And places where I always play,
Look like somewhere else today.

Marie Louise Allen, *A Pocketful of Rhymes*
Harper & Brothers, New York, 1939

FIRST SNOW

Lighter than thistledown
    Blown by a fairy,
Fine flakes of snow fall through
    Space grey and airy.

Whiter than lily that
    Blows sweet in summer,
This first snow of winter,
    This gentle newcomer.

Ivy O. Eastwick, *Fairies and Suchlike*
Published and copyright 1946 by E. P. Dutton & Co., Inc., New York

SNOW
The fenceposts wear marshmallow hats
On a snowy day;
Bushes in their night gowns
Are kneeling down to pray—
And all the trees have silver skirts
And want to dance away.

Dorothy Aldis, *Everything and Anything*
Minton, Balch and Company, New York, 1927
Copyright 1925, 1926, 1927 by Dorothy Aldis

The slushy snow splashes and sploshes,
The snowdrifts come over my feet.
I'm thankful I wore my galoshes
To keep out the ice and the sleet.

Mary Ann Hoberman, *All My Shoes Come in Twos*
Copyright © 1957 by Mary Ann Hoberman and Norman Hoberman
By permission of Little, Brown & Company, Boston

Thin ice
Free advice
Heavy snow
Out you go
Nice slush
Lush lush
Wet feet
Fever heat
Stuffy head
Stay in bed
Who's ill?
Me? A pill?

David McCord, *Far and Few*
Copyright 1929, 1931, 1952 by David McCord
By permission of Little, Brown & Company, Boston

425

CYNTHIA IN THE SNOW

It SUSHES.
It hushes
The loudness in the road.
It flitter-twitters,
And laughs away from me.
It laughs a lovely whiteness,
And whitely whirs away,
To be
Some otherwhere,
Still white as milk or shirts.
So beautiful it hurts.

Gwendolyn Brooks, *Bronzeville Boys and Girls*

SNOW

The snow fell softly all the night.
It made a blanket soft and white.
It covered houses, flowers and ground,
But did not make a single sound!

Alice Wilkins
In *The Golden Flute*
The John Day Company, Inc., New York, 1932

I love snow and all the forms
   Of the radiant frost;
I love waves, and winds, and storms . . .

Percy Bysshe Shelley

SNOW IN THE CITY

Snow is out of fashion,
  But it still comes down,
To whiten all the buildings
  In our town;
To dull the noise of traffic;
  To dim each glaring light
With star-shaped feathers
  Of frosty white.
And not the tallest building
  Halfway up the sky;
Or all the trains and busses,
  And taxis scudding by;
And not a million people,
  Not one of them at all,
Can do a thing about the snow
  But let it fall!

Rachel Field, *Branches Green*

Announced by all the trumpets of the sky,
Arrives the snow, and, driving o'er the fields,
Seems nowhere to alight: the whited air
Hides hills and woods, the river and the heaven,
And veils the farm-house at the garden's end.
The sled and traveller stopped, the courier's feet
Delayed, all friends shut out, the housemates sit
Around the radiant fireplace, enclosed
In a tumultuous privacy of storm.

Ralph Waldo Emerson

AN OLD CHRISTMAS GREETING

Sing hey! Sing hey!
For Christmas Day;
Twine mistletoe and holly,
For friendship glows
In winter snows,
And so let's all be jolly.

Unknown

Heap on more wood!—the wind is chill;
But let it whistle as it will,
We'll keep our Christmas merry still.

Sir Walter Scott

But give me holly, bold and jolly,
Honest, prickly, shining holly;
Pluck me holly leaf and berry
For the day when I make merry.

Christina Georgina Rossetti, *Sing-Song*

BUNDLES

A bundle is a funny thing,
It always sets me wondering;
For whether it is thin or wide
You never know just what's inside.

Especially on Christmas week,
Temptation is so great to peek!
Now wouldn't it be much more fun
If shoppers carried things undone?

John Farrar, *Songs for Parents*
Yale University Press, New Haven, 1921

A VISIT

FROM

ST. NICHOLAS

'Twas the night before Christmas, when all through the house
Not a creature was stirring, not even a mouse;
The stockings were hung by the chimney with care,
In hopes that St. Nicholas soon would be there;
The children were nestled all snug in their beds
While visions of sugar-plums danced in their heads;
And Mamma in her 'kerchief, and I in my cap,
Had just settled our brains for a long winter's nap,
When out on the lawn there arose such a clatter,
I sprang from my bed to see what was the matter.
Away to the window I flew like a flash,
Tore open the shutters and threw up the sash.
The moon on the breast of the new-fallen snow
Gave a lustre of midday to objects below,
When, what to my wondering eyes did appear,
But a miniature sleigh and eight tiny reindeer,
With a little old driver, so lively and quick,
I knew in a moment it must be St. Nick.
More rapid than eagles his coursers they came,
And he whistled, and shouted, and called them by name:
"Now, Dasher! now, Dancer! now, Prancer and Vixen!
On, Comet! on, Cupid! on, Donder and Blitzen!
To the top of the porch! to the top of the wall!
Now dash away! dash away! dash away, all!"
As dry leaves that before the wild hurricane fly,
When they meet with an obstacle, mount to the sky,
So up to the housetop the coursers they flew,

With the sleigh full of toys, and St. Nicholas too.
And then, in a twinkling, I heard on the roof
The prancing and pawing of each little hoof.
As I drew in my head, and was turning around,
Down the chimney St. Nicholas came with a bound.
He was dressed all in fur, from his head to his foot,
And his clothes were all tarnished with ashes and soot;
A bundle of toys he had flung on his back,
And he looked like a peddler just opening his pack.
His eyes—how they twinkled! his dimples, how merry!
His cheeks were like roses, his nose like a cherry!
His droll little mouth was drawn up like a bow,
And the beard on his chin was as white as the snow;
The stump of a pipe he held tight in his teeth,
And the smoke, it encircled his head like a wreath;
He had a broad face and a little round belly
That shook, when he laughed, like a bowl full of jelly.
He was chubby and plump, a right jolly old elf,
And I laughed when I saw him, in spite of myself;
A wink of his eye and a twist of his head,
Soon gave me to know I had nothing to dread;
He spoke not a word, but went straight to his work,
And filled all the stockings; then turned with a jerk,
And laying his finger aside of his nose,
And giving a nod, up the chimney he rose.
He sprang to his sleigh, to his team gave a whistle,
And away they all flew like the down of a thistle.
But I heard him exclaim, ere he drove out of sight,
"HAPPY CHRISTMAS TO ALL,
AND TO ALL A GOOD-NIGHT!"

Clement C. Moore

CONVERSATION BETWEEN
MR. AND MRS. SANTA CLAUS

(Overheard
at the North Pole
Early
Christmas Morning)

"Are the reindeer in the rain, dear?"
Asked Mrs. Santa Claus.
"No. I put them in the barn, dear,
To dry their little paws."

"Is the sleigh, sir, put away, sir,
In the barn beside the deer?"
"Yes, I'm going to get it ready
To use again next year."

"And the pack, dear, is it back, dear?"
"Yes. It's empty of its toys,
And tomorrow I'll start filling it,
For next year's girls and boys."

Rowena Bennett
In *Jack and Jill*, December 1947
Copyright 1947 by The Curtis Publishing Company

CHRISTMAS
CAROL

God bless the master of this house,
　The mistress also,
And all the little children,
　That round the table go,
And all your kin and kinsmen
　That dwell both far and near;
I wish you a Merry Christmas
　And a Happy New Year.

Unknown

431

NEW YEAR'S DAY

Last night, while we were fast asleep,
   The old year went away.
It can't come back again because
   A new one's come to stay.

Rachel Field, *A Little Book of Days*
Copyright 1927 by Doubleday & Company, Inc.

RING OUT, WILD BELLS

Ring out, wild bells, to the wild sky,
   The flying cloud, the frosty light;
   The year is dying in the night;
Ring out, wild bells, and let him die.

Ring out the old, ring in the new,
   Ring, happy bells, across the snow;
   The year is going, let him go;
Ring out the false, ring in the true.

Alfred Tennyson

Cold winter now is in the wood,
The moon wades deep in snow.
Pile balsam boughs about the sills,
And let the fires glow!

The cows must stand in the dark barn,
The horses stamp all day.
Now shall the housewife bake her pies
And keep her kitchen gay.

432

The cat sleeps warm beneath the stove,
The dog on paws outspread;
But the brown deer with flinching hide
Seeks for a sheltered bed.

The fox steps hungry through the brush,
The lean hawk coasts the sky.
"Winter is in the wood!" the winds
In the warm chimney cry.

Elizabeth Coatsworth, *Away Goes Sally*

STOPPING BY WOODS ON A SNOWY EVENING

Whose woods these are I think I know.
His house is in the village though;
He will not see me stopping here
To watch his woods fill up with snow.

My little horse must think it queer
To stop without a farmhouse near
Between the woods and frozen lake
The darkest evening of the year.

He gives his harness bells a shake
To ask if there is some mistake.
The only other sound's the sweep
Of easy wind and downy flake.

The woods are lovely, dark and deep.
But I have promises to keep,
And miles to go before I sleep,
And miles to go before I sleep.

Robert Frost, *New Hampshire*

WAITING

Dreaming of honeycombs to share
With her small cubs, a mother bear
Sleeps in a snug and snowy lair.

Bees in their drowsy, drifted hive
Sip hoarded honey to survive
Until the flowers come alive.

Sleeping beneath the deep snow
Seeds of honeyed flowers know
When it is time to wake and grow.

Harry Behn, *The Little Hill*
Harcourt, Brace and Company, Inc., New York, Copyright 1949

A SURE SIGN

Here's the mail, sort it quick—
Papers, letters, notes,
Postcard scenes,
Magazines;
Our hearts are in our throats.
Something there,
White and square,
Sealed with wax, and bumpy—
At the edges flat and thin,
In the middle lumpy.
When you feel the envelope,
Do your fingers trace
Something narrow,
Like an arrow?
Or a part
Of a heart?
Or a Cupid's face?

Is your name across the back
In a crooked line?
Hurry, then; that's a sign
Someone's sent a valentine!

Nancy Byrd Turner
In *The Youth's Companion*

HEARTS

WERE

MADE TO

GIVE AWAY

Hearts were made to give away
   On Valentine's good day;
Wrap them up in dainty white,
Send them off the thirteenth night,
Any kind of heart that's handy—
   Hearts of lace, and hearts of candy,
   Hearts all trimmed with ribbands fine
   Send for good St. Valentine.
Hearts were made to give away
On Valentine's dear day.

Annette Wynne, *For Days and Days*
Copyright 1919, 1947 by Annette Wynne
Published by J. B. Lippincott Co., Philadelphia

A VALENTINE

Frost flowers on the window glass,
Hopping chickadees that pass,
Bare old elms that bend and sway,
Pussy willows, soft and gray,

Silver clouds across the sky,
Lacy snowflakes flitting by,
Icicles like fringe in line—
That is Outdoor's valentine!

Eleanor Hammond
In *Child Life,* February 1927
Copyright 1927 by Rand McNally & Company
By permission of the author

WISE JOHNNY

Little Johnny-jump-up said,
"It must be spring,
I just saw a lady-bug
And heard a robin sing."

Edwina Fallis
In *Sung under the Silver Umbrella*
The Macmillan Company, New York, 1935

CATKIN

I have a little pussy,
    And her coat is silver gray;
She lives in a great wide meadow
    And she never runs away.
She always is a pussy,
    She'll never be a cat
Because—she's a pussy willow!
    Now what do you think of that!

Unknown

Daffadowndilly
    Has come up to town,
In a yellow petticoat
    And a green gown.

Mother Goose

DAFFODILS

In spite of cold and chills
That usher in the early spring
We have the daffodils.

Kikuriō
From *A Year of Japanese Epigrams*
By permission of Oxford University Press, London

436

Growing in the vale
  By the uplands hilly,
Growing straight and frail,
  Lady Daffadowndilly.

In a golden crown,
And a scant green gown
  While the spring blows chilly,
Lady Daffadown,
  Sweet Daffadowndilly.

Christina Georgina Rossetti, *Sing-Song*

I saw green banks of daffodil,
  Slim poplars in the breeze,
Great tan-brown hares in gusty March
  A-courting on the leas;
And meadows with their glittering streams, and silver scurrying dace,
  Home—what a perfect place!

E. Wyndham Tennant, *Home Thoughts in Laventie*
Published by Oxford University Press, London
By permission of the Estate of the author

. . . daffodils,
That come before the swallow dares, and take
The winds of March with beauty . . .

William Shakespeare

KITE DAYS

A kite, a sky, and a good firm breeze,
And acres of ground away from trees,
And one hundred yards of clean, strong string—
O boy, O boy! I call that Spring!

Mark Sawyer
In *Story Parade*, March 1939
Copyright 1939 by Story Parade, Inc.
and used with their permission

SPRING

The last snow is going,
Brooks are overflowing,
And a sunny wind is blowing
   Swiftly along.

Through the sky birds are blowing,
On earth green is showing,
You can feel earth growing
   So quiet and strong.

A sunny wind is blowing,
Farmer's busy sowing,
Apple trees are snowing,
   And shadows grow long.

Now the wind is slowing,
Cows begin lowing,
Evening clouds are glowing
   And dusk is full of song.

Harry Behn, *The Little Hill*
Harcourt, Brace and Company, Inc., New York, Copyright 1949

For, lo, the winter is past,
The rain is over and gone;
The flowers appear on the earth;
The time of the singing of birds is come,
And the voice of the turtle is heard in our land.

The Song of Songs

ROBIN'S SONG

Robin's song is crystal clear
Cold as an icicle,
Sharp as a spear.
I have seen Spring lift her head,
Snowdrops a-shivering,
Winter dead.

E. L. M. King, *Fifty Country Rhymes for Children*
Copyright 1926 by D. Appleton and Company
Reprinted by permission of Appleton-Century-Crofts, Inc.

WRITTEN IN MARCH

The Cock is crowing,
The stream is flowing,
The small birds twitter,
The lake doth glitter,
The green field sleeps in the sun;
The oldest and youngest
Are at work with the strongest;
The cattle are grazing,
Their heads never raising;
There are forty feeding like one!

Like an army defeated
The snow hath retreated,
And now doth fare ill
On the top of the bare hill;
The ploughboy is whooping—anon—anon:
There's joy in the mountains;
There's life in the fountains;
Small clouds are sailing,
Blue sky prevailing;
The rain is over and gone!

William Wordsworth

439

CROCUSES

The sunrise tints the dew;
The yellow crocuses are out,
And I must pick a few.

Jōsa
From *A Year of Japanese Epigrams*
By permission of Oxford University Press, London

APRIL

The roofs are shining from the rain,
The sparrows twitter as they fly,
And with a windy April grace
The little clouds go by.

Yet the back-yards are bare and brown
With only one unchanging tree—
I could not be so sure of Spring
Save that it sings in me.

Sara Teasdale, *Rivers to the Sea*
Copyright 1915, 1943 by The Macmillan Company
and used with their permission

APRIL

PUDDLE

The rain falls down upon the grass
And makes a silver looking glass,
So all the buds may bend and see
What kind of flowers they will be.

Rowena Bennett
In *Boys and Girls Today*, May 1941
Copyright 1941 by The Methodist Publishing House
By permission of the author

APRIL SHOWERS

The leaves are fresh after the rain,
The air is sweet and clear,
The sun is shining warm again,
The sparrows hopping in the lane
Are brisk and full of cheer.

And that is why we dance and play,
And that is why we sing,
Calling out in voices gay,
We will not go to school to-day
Nor learn anything!

It is a happy thing, I say,
To be alive on such a day.

James Stephens, *Collected Poems*
Copyright 1941 by James Stephens
Used by permission of The Macmillan Company, New York
Macmillan & Company, Ltd., London
and Mrs. James Stephens

EASTER

The air is like a butterfly
    With frail blue wings.
The happy earth looks at the sky
    And sings.

Joyce Kilmer, *Poems, Essays and Letters*
Copyright 1914, 1917, 1918 by Doubleday & Company, Inc.

LILIES

I thought I saw white clouds, but no!—
    Bending across the fence,
    White lilies in a row!

Shikō
From *Little Pictures of Japan*
arranged by Olive Beaupré Miller
By permission of the arranger and the publishers,
The Book House for Children, Lake Bluff, Illinois

441

MEETING THE EASTER BUNNY

On Easter morn at early dawn
  before the cocks were crowing,
I met a bob-tail bunnykin
  and asked where he was going,
" 'Tis in the house and out the house
  a-tipsy, tipsy-toeing,
'Tis round the house and 'bout the house
  a-lightly I am going."
"But what is that of every hue
  you carry in your basket?"
" 'Tis eggs of gold and eggs of blue;
  I wonder that you ask it.
'Tis chocolate eggs and bonbon eggs
  and eggs of red and gray,
For every child in every house
  on bonny Easter Day."
He perked his ears and winked his eye
  and twitched his little nose;
He shook his tail—what tail he had—
  and stood up on his toes.
"I must be gone before the sun;
  the east is growing gray;
'Tis almost time for bells to chime."—
  So he hippety-hopped away.

Rowena Bennett, *Songs from Around a Toadstool Table*
Follett Publishing Company, Chicago, 1930

EASTER SNOWFALL

Days after daffodils were up
And some of them were showing gold,
And I had found a buttercup—
Without the weather turning cold
Quietly it snowed all night.
At sunrise when I saw the ground
And grass and fences glittering white,
And every bush a little mound,
It didn't seem at all like Spring,
Or winter either, but a wide
And sparkly egg the bunnies bring
At Easter with the world inside!

Harry Behn, *The Wizard in the Well*

THE FALL OF THE PLUM BLOSSOMS

I came to look, and lo!
The plum tree petals scatter down,
A fall of purest snow.

Rankō

THE IRIS

Ere yet the sun is high,
All blue the iris blossoms wave,
The colour of the sky.

Gasetsu

Oh, fair to see
Bloom-laden cherry tree,
  Arrayed in sunny white:
  An April day's delight,
Oh, fair to see!

Oh, fair to see
Fruit-laden cherry tree,
  With balls of shining red
  Decking a leafy head,
Oh, fair to see!

Christina Georgina Rossetti, *Sing-Song*

Under the greenwood tree
Who loves to lie with me,
And turn his merry note
Unto the sweet bird's throat,
Come hither, come hither, come hither:
  Here shall he see
  No enemy
But winter and rough weather.

William Shakespeare

TREES

Trees are the kindest things I know,
They do no harm, they simply grow

And spread a shade for sleepy cows,
And gather birds among their boughs.

They give us fruit in leaves above,
And wood to make our houses of,

And leaves to burn on Hallowe'en,
And in the Spring new buds of green.

They are the first when day's begun
To touch the beams of morning sun,

They are the last to hold the light
When evening changes into night,

And when a moon floats on the sky
They hum a drowsy lullaby

Of sleepy children long ago . . .
Trees are the kindest things I know.

Harry Behn, *The Little Hill*
Harcourt, Brace and Company, Inc., New York, Copyright 1949

WHAT DO WE PLANT?

What do we plant when we plant the tree?
We plant the ship, which will cross the sea.
We plant the mast to carry the sails;
We plant the planks to withstand the gales—
The keel, the keelson, and beam and knee;
We plant the ship when we plant the tree.

What do we plant when we plant the tree?
We plant the houses for you and me.
We plant the rafters, the shingles, the floors,
We plant the studding, the lath, the doors,
The beams and siding, all parts that be;
We plant the house when we plant the tree.

What do we plant when we plant the tree?
A thousand things that we daily see;
We plant the spire that out-towers the crag,
We plant the staff for our country's flag,
We plant the shade, from the hot sun free;
We plant all these when we plant the tree.

Henry Abbey, *The Poems of Henry Abbey*
D. Appleton and Company, New York, 1904

SPRING

The leaves are uncurling,
My seedlings are up,
The sunlight is warmer,
We've got a new pup.
The robins are building,
I've painted my bike,
And we can go barefoot
Whenever we like.

Marchette Chute

Copyright 1941 by Marchette Chute
From *Around and About* by Marchette Chute
Published by E. P. Dutton & Co., Inc., New York, 1957

SEEDS

The seeds I sowed—
For weeks unseen—
Have pushed up pygmy
Shoots of green;
So frail you'd think
The tiniest stone
Would never let
A glimpse be shown.

But no; a pebble
Near them lies,
At least a cherry-stone
In size,
Which that mere sprout
Has heaved away,
To bask in sun,
And see the day.

Walter de la Mare, *Rhymes and Verses*

Published by Henry Holt & Company, Inc., New York, 1947
By permission of the literary trustees of Walter de la Mare
and The Society of Authors, London, as their representatives

446

The days are clear,
   Day after day,
When April's here,
   That leads to May,
And June
Must follow soon:
   Stay, June, stay!—
If only we could stop the moon
And June!

Christina Georgina Rossetti, Sing-Song

There is but one May in the year,
   And sometimes May is wet and cold;
There is but one May in the year
   Before the year grows old.

Yet though it be the chilliest May,
   With least of sun and most of showers,
Its wind and dew, its night and day,
   Bring up the flowers.

Christina Georgina Rossetti, Sing-Song

HERE WE COME A-PIPING

Here we come a-piping,
In Springtime and in May;
Green fruit a-ripening,
And Winter fled away.
The Queen she sits upon the strand,
Fair as lily, white as wand;
Seven billows on the sea,
Horses riding fast and free,
And bells beyond the sand.

Unknown

To-day I saw a butterfly,
    The first-born of the spring,
Sunning itself upon a bank—
    A lovely tawny thing.

I saw a dandelion, too,
    As golden as the sun;
And these will still be beautiful
    When all the wars are done.

Teresa Hooley, "Beauty Eternal" in *Selected Poems*
Published by Jonathan Cape, Ltd., London, 1947
By permission of the author

DANDELION

O little soldier with the golden helmet,
What are you guarding on my lawn?
You with your green gun
And your yellow beard,
Why do you stand so stiff?
There is only the grass to fight!

Hilda Conkling, *Poems by a Little Girl*
Copyright 1920 by J. B. Lippincott Company

DANDELIONS

Over the climbing meadows
Where swallow-shadows float,
These are the small gold buttons
On earth's green, windy coat.

Frances Frost, *Pool in the Meadow*
Reprinted by permission of and arrangement with
Houghton Mifflin Company, the authorized publishers

MILLIONS OF STRAWBERRIES

Marcia and I went over the curve,
Eating our way down
Jewels of strawberries we didn't deserve,
Eating our way down.
Till our hands were sticky, and our lips painted,
And over us the hot day fainted,
And we saw snakes,
And got scratched,
And a lust overcame us for the red unmatched
Small buds of berries,
Till we lay down—
Eating our way down—
And rolled in the berries like two little dogs,
Rolled
In the late gold.
And gnats hummed,
And it was cold,
And home we went, home without a berry,
Painted red and brown,
Eating our way down.

Genevieve Taggard

In *The New Yorker*, June 8, 1929
The New Yorker Magazine, Inc., New York

SPRINKLING

Sometimes in the summer
When the day is hot
Daddy takes the garden hose
And finds a shady spot;
Then he calls me over,
Looks at my bare toes
And says, "Why, you need sprinkling,
You thirsty little rose!"

Dorothy Mason Pierce

In *Sung under the Silver Umbrella*
The Macmillan Company, New York, 1935

THE LITTLE

ROSE TREE

Every rose on the little tree
Is making a different face at me!

Some look surprised when I pass by,
And others droop—but they are shy.

These two whose heads together press
Tell secrets I could never guess.

Some have their heads thrown back to sing,
And all the buds are listening.

I wonder if the gardener knows,
Or if he calls each just a rose?

Rachel Field, *The Pointed People*
The Macmillan Company, New York, 1930

I'VE

GOT A

ROCKET

I've got a rocket
In my pocket;
I cannot stop to play.
Away it goes!
I've burnt my toes.
It's Independence Day.

Unknown

FOURTH

OF JULY

NIGHT

Pin wheels whirling round
Spit sparks upon the ground,
And rockets shoot up high
And blossom in the sky—
Blue and yellow, green and red
Flowers falling on my head,
And I don't ever have to go
To bed, to bed, to bed!

Dorothy Aldis, *Hop, Skip and Jump*
Minton, Balch and Company, New York, 1934
Copyright 1934 by Dorothy Aldis

What is pink? a rose is pink
By the fountain's brink.
What is red? a poppy's red
In its barley bed.
What is blue? the sky is blue
Where the clouds float thro'.
What is white? a swan is white
Sailing in the light.
What is yellow? pears are yellow,
Rich and ripe and mellow.
What is green? the grass is green,
With small flowers between.
What is violet? clouds are violet
In the summer twilight.
What is orange? why, an orange,
Just an orange!

Christina Georgina Rossetti, *Sing-Song*

VEGETABLES

The country vegetables scorn
    To lie about in shops,
They stand upright as they were born
    In neatly-patterned crops;

And when you want your dinner you
    Don't buy it from a shelf,
You find a lettuce fresh with dew
    And pull it for yourself;

You pick an apronful of peas
    And shell them on the spot,
You cut a cabbage, if you please,
    To pop into the pot.

The folk who their potatoes buy
    From sacks before they sup,
Miss half of the potato's joy,
    And that's to dig it up.

Eleanor Farjeon, *Poems for Children*

Copyright 1951 by Eleanor Farjeon
Published by J. B. Lippincott Co., Philadelphia

LABOR

OF

FIELDS

July is honored with the labor of fields
That round against the sky in standing grain,
So beautiful the breath comes quick to see them.
It is the month men pray for little rain
So they may cut their hay and spread it out
Tossing it over for the sun to dry
And bring it safely to the empty barns
Before the clouds have massed too dark and high.

It is the month of sweat and weariness,
Of the arm aching with the scythe's slow weight,
Of horses straining heavily up the road
Through lengthening shadows as the hour grows late.
In river lowlands, ledged fields by the sea,
And sloping inland valleys far away
The old laborious ritual is performed—
Once more, once more men gather in the hay.

Elizabeth Coatsworth, *Country Poems*

I WILL GO WITH MY FATHER A-PLOUGHING

I will go with my Father a-ploughing
To the Green Field by the sea,
And the rooks and crows and seagulls
Will come flocking after me.
I will sing to the patient horses
With the lark in the shine of the air,
And my Father will sing the Plough-Song
That blesses the cleaving share.

I will go with my Father a-sowing
To the Red Field by the sea,
And blackbirds and robins and thrushes
Will come flocking after me.
I will sing to the striding sowers
With the finch on the flowering sloe,
And my Father will sing the Seed-Song
That only the wise men know.

I will go with my Father a-reaping
To the Brown Field by the sea,
And the geese and pigeons and sparrows
Will come flocking after me.
I will sing to the weary reapers
With the wren in the heat of the sun,
And my Father will sing the Scythe-Song
That joys for the harvest done.

Joseph Campbell, *The Mountainy Singer*
Published by The Four Seas Company, Boston, 1919

WISDOM
AND
BEAUTY

9

Look for a lovely thing and you will
    find it,
It is not far—
    It never will be far.

HAPPY THOUGHT

The world is so full of a number of things,
I'm sure we should all be as happy as kings.

Robert Louis Stevenson, *A Child's Garden of Verses*

THE WONDERFUL WORLD

Great, wide, beautiful, wonderful World,
With the wonderful water round you curled,
And the wonderful grass upon your breast,
World, you are beautifully dressed.

The wonderful air is over me,
And the wonderful wind is shaking the tree—
It walks on the water, and whirls the mills,
And talks to itself on the top of the hills.

You friendly Earth, how far do you go,
With the wheat fields that nod and the rivers that flow,
With cities and gardens and cliffs and isles,
And the people upon you for thousands of miles?

Ah! you are so great, and I am so small,
I hardly can think of you, World, at all;
And yet, when I said my prayers today,
My mother kissed me, and said, quite gay,

"If the wonderful World is great to you,
And great to Father and Mother, too,
You are more than the Earth, though you are such a dot!
You can love and think, and the Earth cannot!"

William Brighty Rands

456

Atom from atom yawns as far
As moon from earth, or star from star.

Ralph Waldo Emerson

I AM

I am willowy boughs
For coolness;
I am gold-finch wings
For darkness;
I am a little grape
Thinking of September,
I am a very small violet
Thinking of May.

Hilda Conkling, Poems by a Little Girl

LESSON

To plant a seed and see it grow
Is something every child should do,

And when it blossoms, how it grew
Is something every child should know,

And when its seeds are ripe to sow,
A child may see the old made new.

To grow and gently grow and grow
Is something people should do too.

Harry Behn, Windy Morning

457

A LITTLE SONG OF LIFE

Glad that I live am I;
That the sky is blue;
Glad for the country lanes,
And the fall of dew.

After the sun the rain;
After the rain the sun;
This is the way of life,
Till the work be done.

All that we need to do,
Be we low or high,
Is to see that we grow
Nearer the sky.

Lizette Woodworth Reese, *A Wayside Lute*
Thomas B. Mosher, Portland, Maine, 1909

LESSONS

From a Sun-Dial

Ignore dull days; forget the showers;
Keep count of only shining hours.

Day-Dreamer

Too much thought:
Too little wrought.

Motto

However they talk, whatever they say,
Look straight at the task without dismay—
And if you can do it, do it today.

Short Sermon

To give—and forgive—
Is a good way to live.

From the German adapted by Louis Untermeyer
In *Rainbow in the Sky*
Harcourt, Brace and Company, Inc., New York, Copyright 1935

458

PROVERBS

Of Quarrels
No Quarrel ever Stirred
   Before the Second Word.

Of Giving
Not what you Get, but what you Give
   Is that which proves your Right to Live.

Of Courtesy
Good Manners may in Seven Words be found:
Forget Yourself and think of Those Around.

OTHERS

Even though it's raining
I don't wish it wouldn't.
That would be like saying
I think it shouldn't.
I'd rather be out playing
Than sitting hours and hours
Watching rain falling
In drips and drops and showers,
But what about the robins?
What about the flowers?

He who has never known hunger
Has never known how good
The taste of bread may be,
The kindliness of food.

An emerald is as green as grass;
  A ruby red as blood;
A sapphire shines as blue as heaven;
  A flint lies in the mud.

A diamond is a brilliant stone,
  To catch the world's desire;
An opal holds a fiery spark;
  But a flint holds fire.

Christina Georgina Rossetti, *Sing-Song*

Violets, daffodils,
Roses and thorn
Were all in the garden
Before you were born.

Daffodils, violets,
Green thorn and roses
Your grandchildren's children
Will hold to their noses.

Elizabeth Coatsworth, *The Littlest House*

The world turns and the world changes,
But one thing does not change.
In all of my years, one thing does not change.
However you disguise it, this thing does not change:
The perpetual struggle of Good and Evil.

T. S. Eliot, from "The Rock," in *Collected Poems*

LOVELINESS

Loveliness that dies when I forget
Comes alive when I remember.

Hilda Conkling, *Shoes of the Wind*
Copyright 1922 by J. B. Lippincott Company

NIGHT

Stars over snow,
    And in the west a planet
Swinging below a star—
    Look for a lovely thing and you will find it,
It is not far—
    It never will be far.

Sara Teasdale, *Stars To-Night*
Copyright 1930, 1958 by Sara Teasdale Filsinger
By permission of The Macmillan Company, New York

BE LIKE THE BIRD

Be like the bird, who
Halting in his flight
On limb too slight
Feels it give way beneath him,
Yet sings
Knowing he hath wings.

Victor Hugo

A BLACKBIRD SUDDENLY

Heaven is in my hand, and I
Touch a heart-beat of the sky,
Hearing a blackbird's cry.

Strange, beautiful, unquiet thing,
Lone flute of God, how can you sing
Winter to spring?

You have outdistanced every voice and word,
And given my spirit wings until it stirred
Like you—a bird!

Joseph Auslander, *Sunrise Trumpets*
Copyright 1924 by Harper & Brothers

DUST OF SNOW

The way a crow
Shook down on me
The dust of snow
From a hemlock tree

Has given my heart
A change of mood
And saved some part
Of a day I had rued.

Robert Frost, *New Hampshire*
Copyright 1923 by Henry Holt and Company, Inc.
Used by permission of the publishers

DAYS

Some days my thoughts are just cocoons—all cold, and dull and
    blind,
They hang from dripping branches in the grey woods of my mind;
And other days they drift and shine—such free and flying things!
I find the gold-dust in my hair, left by their brushing wings.

Karle Wilson Baker, *Blue Smoke*
Yale University Press, New Haven, 1919

THE COIN

Into my heart's treasury
    I slipped a coin
That time cannot take
    Nor a thief purloin,—
Oh, better than the minting
    Of a gold-crowned king
Is the safe-kept memory
    Of a lovely thing.

Sara Teasdale, *Flame and Shadow*
Copyright 1920, 1948 by The Macmillan Company
and used with their permission

LEISURE

What is this life if, full of care,
We have no time to stand and stare.

No time to stand beneath the boughs
And stare as long as sheep or cows.

No time to see, when woods we pass,
Where squirrels hide their nuts in grass.

No time to see, in broad daylight,
Streams full of stars, like stars at night.

No time to turn at Beauty's glance,
And watch her feet, how they can dance.

No time to wait till her mouth can
Enrich that smile her eyes began.

A poor life this if, full of care,
We have no time to stand and stare.

William Henry Davies
The Collected Poems of William H. Davies
Jonathan Cape & Harrison Smith, New York, 1929

SONG

The primrose in the green forest,
    The violets they be gay;
The double daisies, and the rest
That trimly decks the way,
Doth move the spirits with brave delights,
    Who Beauty's darlings be.

Thomas Deloney

A CHARM FOR SPRING FLOWERS

Who sees the first marsh marigold
Shall count more wealth than hands can hold.

Who bends a knee where violets grow
A hundred secret things shall know.

Who finds hepatica's dim blue
Shall have his dearest wish come true.

Who spies on lady-slippers fair
Shall keep a heart as light as air.

But whosoever toucheth not
One petal, sets no root in pot,

He shall be blessed of earth and sky
Till under them he, too, shall lie.

Rachel Field, *Poems*

BEAUTY

Beauty is seen
In the sunlight,
The trees, the birds,
Corn growing and people working
Or dancing for their harvest.

Beauty is heard
In the night,
Wind sighing, rain falling,
Or a singer chanting
Anything in earnest.

Beauty is in yourself.
Good deeds, happy thoughts

That repeat themselves
In your dreams,
In your work,
And even in your rest.

WE

WHO

WERE

BORN

We who were born
In country places,
Far from cities
And shifting faces,
We have a birthright
No man can sell,
And a secret joy
No man can tell.

For we are kindred
To lordly things:
The wild duck's flight
And the white owl's wings,
To pike and salmon,
To bull and horse,
The curlew's cry
And the smell of gorse.

Pride of trees,
Swiftness of streams,
Magic of frost
Have shaped our dreams.
No baser vision
Their spirit fills
Who walk by right
On the naked hills.

465

MY
LAND IS
FAIR
FOR ANY
EYES
TO SEE

My land is fair for any eyes to see—
Now look, my friends—look to the east and west!
You see the purple hills far in the west—
Hills lined with pine and gum and black-oak tree—
Now to the east you see the fertile valley!
This land is mine, I sing of it to you—
My land beneath the skies of white and blue.
This land is mine, for I am part of it.
I am the land, for it is part of me—
We are akin and thus our kinship be!
It would make me a brother to the tree!
And far as eyes can see this land is mine.
Not for one foot of it I have a deed—
To own this land I do not need a deed—
They all belong to me—gum, oak, and pine.

Oh, I have seen the winter desolate-gray
Hang months and months over the barren lands,
I've heard the winter winds blow through the trees,
Blow through the icy heavens filled with leaves.

We felt secure, housed with fruits of the land—
We felt secure—no one can understand
How fine it is to live close to the land—
To neighbors in distress we lent a hand.
We saw the crows go flying cross the land,
Up in the icy heavens with the leaves,
We saw the crows fly over gray-starved land
When winter winds sighed in the last year leaves.
And cozily we sat by our fireside
And ate of corn and supped of berry-wine;
We sat and let the snow-world drift outside;
We sat and watched through frosted window panes
The snow flakes drifting through green tops of pine.

Jesse Stuart, *Man with a Bull-Tongue Plow*
Published by E. P. Dutton & Co., Inc., New York, 1934
By permission of the author

HOLD FAST YOUR DREAMS

Within your heart
Keep one still, secret spot
Where dreams may go,
And sheltered so,
May thrive and grow—
Where doubt and fear are not.
Oh, keep a place apart
Within your heart,
For little dreams to go.

Louise Driscoll
By permission of the author

HEAVEN

Heaven is
The place where
Happiness is
Everywhere.

 If humility and purity be not in the heart, they
are not in the home: and if they are not
in the home, they are not in the City.

WHO

HATH A

BOOK

Who hath a book
    Hath friends at hand,
And gold and gear
    At his command;
And rich estates,
    If he but look,
Are held by him
    Who hath a book.

Who hath a book
    Hath but to read
And he may be
    A king, indeed.
His kingdom is
    His inglenook—
All this is his
    Who hath a book.

Wilbur D. Nesbit, *A Book of Poems*

468

WISDOM

I stand most humbly
Before man's wisdom,
Knowing we are not
Really wise:

If we were
We'd open up the kingdom
And make earth happy
As the dreamed of skies.

Langston Hughes, *Fields of Wonder*

I believe a leaf of grass is no less than the journey-work of the stars,
And the pismire is equally perfect, and a grain of sand, and the egg
    of the wren,
And the tree-toad is a chef-d'oeuvre for the highest,
And the running blackberry would adorn the parlors of heaven,
And the narrowest hinge in my hand puts to scorn all machinery,
And the cow crunching with depress'd head surpasses any statue,
And a mouse is miracle enough to stagger sextillions of infidels.

Walt Whitman

How gray the rain
And gray the world
And gray the rain clouds overhead,
When suddenly
Some cloud is furled
And there is gleaming sun instead!

The raindrops drip
Prismatic light,
And trees and meadows burn in green,
And arched in air
Serene and bright
The rainbow all at once is seen.

Serene and bright
The rainbow stands
That was not anywhere before,
And so may joy
Fill empty hands
When someone enters through a door.

Elizabeth Coatsworth, *Five Bushel Farm*

The warm of heart shall never lack a fire
However far he roam.
Although he live forever among strangers
He cannot lack a home.

For strangers are not strangers to his spirit,
And each house seems his own,
And by the fire of his loving-kindness
He cannot sit alone.

Elizabeth Coatsworth, *Five Bushel Farm*
Copyright 1939 by The Macmillan Company
and used with their permission

HOUSE BLESSING

Bless the four corners of this house,
    And be the lintel blest;
And bless the hearth and bless the board
    And bless each place of rest;
And bless the door that opens wide
    To stranger as to kin;
And bless each crystal window-pane
    That lets the starlight in;
And bless the rooftree overhead
    And every sturdy wall.
The peace of man, the peace of God,
    The peace of Love on all!

Arthur Guiterman
Death and General Putnam and 101 Other Poems
Published and copyright 1935
by E. P. Dutton & Co., Inc., New York

GOOD NIGHT

Good night! good night!
Far flies the light;
But still God's love
Shall flame above,
Making all bright.
Good night! Good night!

Victor Hugo

INDEX
OF
AUTHORS

475

481

INDEX

OF

TITLES

484

485

486

490

491

494

496

INDEX

OF

FIRST LINES

501

511